Help with Homework

English essentials
get to grips with English

Key Stage 2

9+
years

Helpful hints for parents

- Start at the beginning of the book and try to work through the activities in order. Keep the sessions fairly short and work at your child's pace.

- Give lots of encouragement.

- Help your child to work independently as much as possible, without referring to the answers!

- Discuss any areas that your child finds particularly tricky and don't worry if your child finds any of the exercises too difficult. Remember, children learn different things at different rates.

www.autumnchildrensbooks.co.uk

Know your nouns

A **noun** is a person, place or thing.

The sentences below don't make sense because the nouns are incorrect. Cross out the noun (underlined) and replace it with a noun from the box.

1. I hurt my <u>hair</u>. _____

2. The <u>river</u> is still wet. _____

3. Don't touch the <u>clouds</u>! _____

4. Red is my favourite <u>dish</u>. _____

5. Can I have a <u>lion</u>? _____

6. Let's go for a <u>sky</u>. _____

Nouns:

| walk | exhibits | paint |
| colour | biscuit | knee |

GET IT?

The word 'walk' can be a noun or a verb depending on how it is used in the sentence, eg 'a walk' is a noun but 'he walks' is a verb. If you can write 'a' or 'an' before the word then it is usually a noun.

A **collective noun** is a word given to a group of things, eg a **team** of footballers.

Choose a collective noun from the list to complete these phrases.

1. a _____ of dolphins

2. a _____ of fish

3. a _____ of ants

4. a _____ of people

5. a _____ of stars

6. a _____ of ships

7. a _____ of eggs

8. a _____ of puppies

Collective nouns:

colony	pod	litter
fleet	shoal	galaxy
crowd	clutch	

Perfect your pronouns

Pronouns are useful because they can be used instead of repeating a noun.

Replace the nouns (underlined below) with personal pronouns from the box.

1. The reds beat the blues. **The reds** won by two points. _____

2. Jack loved the film when **Jack** saw **the film**. _____

3. Bella is in my class. Do you know **Bella**? _____

4. Our neighbours are friendly when you get to know **our neighbours**. _____

Personal pronouns:

I	they / them
we / us	it
you	he / she
him/her	

Possessive pronouns tell you who owns something, eg The bike belongs to Tom. It's **his**.

Choose possessive pronouns to complete the following sentences:

1. The ice cream belongs to Amy. It's _____ .

2. The snake belongs to us. It's _____ .

3. The hat belongs to you. It's _____ .

4. The car belongs to them. It's _____ .

Possessive pronouns:

mine / ours	theirs
his / hers	its
yours	

Adding adjectives

An **adjective** is a describing word that tells you more about a noun.

For example, a building… a **new** building… a **wonderful, new** building

Underline the adjectives in the sentences below.

1. The clever detective caught the notorious thief.

2. Spectacular fireworks lit up the dark sky.

3. A big, hairy spider sat beside the little boy.

GET IT?

Adding adjectives before the noun will make your writing more interesting and informative for the reader.

Add adjectives before the nouns in these sentences. Write on the lines below.

1. The dog chased the cat.

_____

2. We had a meal in a restaurant.

_____

3. She wore a dress and shoes.

_____

Comparing adjectives

Compare these adjectives. The first one has been done for you.

	er	est
small	smaller	smallest
big	_____	_____
loud	_____	_____
funny	_____	_____
healthy	_____	_____

Sometimes we make a comparison by using **more**, **less** or **most** before an adjective.

less beautiful	**more beautiful**	**most beautiful**
less efficient	**more efficient**	**most efficient**

Underline the comparative adjectives in these sentences.

1. The triceratops was heavier than two elephants.

2. Energy-saving bulbs last longer than ordinary bulbs.

3. Wind energy is greener than oil.

4. Vegetables are healthier than cakes.

5. Of all the jellyfish, the box jellyfish is the most deadly.

Verbs and adverbs

A **verb** is a doing word. It tells us about the action taking place.

Which of these sentences sounds the most interesting?

WEAK VERB

1. The boy **went** across the field.

BETTER VERB

2. The boy **ran** across the field.

VERB + ADVERB

3. The boy **ran quickly** across the field.

POWERFUL VERB

4. The boy **sprinted** across the field.

GET IT?

The sentence with the powerful verb is the most interesting. It is better to use one powerful word rather than lots of weaker ones.

Think of more powerful verbs to replace those underlined below.

1. The car <u>went</u> down the road. _____

2. The mouse <u>went</u> under the sofa. _____

3. The waves <u>went</u> onto the rocks. _____

4. The girl <u>went</u> down the corridor. _____

5. The boy <u>went</u> into the cave. _____

An **adverb** will tell us more about a verb.

Write an adverb after these verbs. Choose from the box or use your own.

1. He looked _____ at his opponent.

2. They spoke _____ on the phone.

3. She sang _____ into the microphone.

4. The wind blew _____ .

5. The volcano erupted _____ .

Adverbs:

fiercely	quietly
angrily	jokingly
softly	violently
kindly	loudly
suddenly	gently

GET IT?

An adverb can change the meaning of the verb. For example, someone can look **suspiciously** or look **curiously** around a room.

Playing with words

Similes are when you describe something as being <u>like</u> something else.

For example, the rocks were jagged **like shark's teeth**.

Make up some of your own similes to complete these descriptions:

1. The crashing waves were like _____

2. The hot sun was like _____

3. The autumn leaves were like _____

4. The tiger's eyes were like _____

Metaphors are when you say that something <u>is</u> something else.

For example, She's a clown! (She is someone who is always joking.)

Choose a metaphor to describe these people or things.

1. someone who is always smiling _____

2. someone who is sneaky _____

3. a tiny flaw that spoils something _____

4. someone who stays up late _____

Metaphors:

a snake in the grass   a ray of sunshine

a fly in the ointment   a night owl

Proverbs are common sayings or comments about life.

Write what you think these proverbs mean:

1. The grass is always greener on the other side.

_____

2. Don't put all your eggs in one basket.

_____

3. Two heads are better than one.

_____

4. Better late than never!

_____

5. All that glitters is not gold.

Onomatopoeia is a word that sounds like the thing it is describing.

BUZZ! CRASH! POP! GLUG! SQUELCH! PLOP! SQUEAK!

Write some more examples of onomatopoeia:

Palindromes are words that read the same backwards and forwards.

For example, Anna, mum, dad.

Write some more palindromes:

_____

Full stops and capitals

We put **full stops** (.) in sentences in places where we would pause when reading the words.

Read the following passage and add full stops where you think the pauses should be.

> i wake up each morning before the alarm i wait for it to ring on the dot of seven and then i get up but today was going to be different i didn't wake up the alarm didn't ring this difference would change my life forever

Go back to the same passage above and add capital letters for 'I', and for the start of each sentence.

Now check against the following text:

> I wake up each morning before the alarm. I wait for it to ring on the dot of seven and then I get up. But today was going to be different. I didn't wake up. The alarm didn't ring. This difference would change my life forever.

How did you score? Give yourself one point for each correct full stop and capital letter.

my score _____

Semicolons and colons

A **semicolon** (;) joins parts of a sentence where there are closely connected ideas.

For example:

I didn't wake up; the alarm didn't ring.

Write a sentence that contains a semicolon. Use it to link your ideas together.

_____

Colons (:) appear at the start of a list or just before an idea.

For example:

To make my favourite sandwich you will need: bread, margarine, tuna and cucumber.

If you are writing a complicated list, you can use semicolons to help you separate the items.

For example:

To make my favourite sandwich, you will need: wholemeal or brown bread, cut into two slices; thinly-sliced cucumber; drained tuna flakes; and reduced-fat, low-salt margarine.

Write a list of ingredients (starting with a colon) for your favourite sandwich. Add commas and/or semicolons to separate items in the list.

For my favourite sandwich, you will need

_____

How to use apostrophes

Apostrophes have two important jobs:

1. An apostrophe tells you who owns what – this is called **possession**. For example, the shark's teeth (the teeth belonging to the shark).

2. An apostrophe tells you which words are shortened – this is called **contraction**. For example, It's a shark! (It is a shark!).

Write a phrase containing a possessive apostrophe for each of the statements below.

The first one has been done for you.

1. the desk belonging to the teacher   *the teacher's desk*

2. the purse belonging to Mum

3. the studio belonging to the artist

4. the whiskers belonging to the cat

Now check out the 'get it' at the top of the next page before you do the questions below.

Write a phrase containing a plural possessive apostrophe for the statements below.

The first one has been done for you.

1. the dog belonging to the girls   *the girls' dog*

2. the car belonging to the family

3. the changing room belonging to the players

4. the jobs belonging to the people

5. the toys belonging to the babies

Apostrophes are also used when you want to shorten words or phrases. The apostrophe replaces the missing letters.

Learn these contractions:

I am – **I'm**

he is / she is – **he's / she's**

it is – **it's**

you are – **you're**

they are – **they're**

we are – **we're**

do not – **don't**

did not – **didn't**

does not – **doesn't**

cannot – **can't**

could not – **couldn't**

would not – **wouldn't**

Use an apostrophe to shorten words in each of the sentences below.

The first one has been done for you.

1. We cannot go yet.   We can't go yet.

2. She did not like the taste.   _____

3. The dog does not bite.   _____

4. The car will not start.   _____

5. It is not fair!   _____

Speech!

Speech marks (" ") tell you exactly what words are spoken by the characters in a story.

Read the story extract and draw speech marks around the words that are said by the characters.

I think Benji is sick, said Tom. He won't eat his dinner.

Perhaps he's not hungry, replied Tom's mum.

But he's *always* hungry! said Tom. And it's his favourite: marinated chicken chunks in juicy jelly.

Continue the conversation between Tom and his mum on the lines below. Start a new line for each new speaker. Draw speech marks around the words that are spoken.

_____

_____

_____

_____

_____

_____

Conversation often has question marks or exclamation marks.

Question marks (?) tell you that a question is being asked.

Exclamation marks (!) show surprise, humour or excitement.

Read the story extract. Change the punctuation by substituting question marks or exclamation marks where you think they belong.

"Mum," shouted Tom.

"Now what," said Tom's mum.

"I know why Benji won't eat his dinner," said Tom. "It's a new recipe. They've added vegetables. You know he hates vegetables."

Continue the conversation between Tom and his mum on the lines below. Include speech marks, question marks and exclamation marks where necessary.

_____

_____

_____

_____

_____

_____

Clauses and conjunctions

A sentence or a clause has to include a noun and a verb.

For example:
Benji loves chicken.

Benji is a noun and **loves** is a verb.

A **conjunction** is a connecting word (sometimes called a connective) that links clauses or sentences.

Conjunctions:	
and	or
but	because
so	when
if	while

For example:
Benji loves chicken. He hates vegetables.
Benji loves chicken **but** he hates vegetables.

Use a conjunction to write one sentence each time.

1. Benji didn't eat his dinner. Bob ate it instead.

_____

2. Benji and Bob were friends. They were rivals too.

_____

3. Tom was worried. Benji didn't eat.

_____

4. Mum wasn't paying attention. She was busy.

_____

Write a sentence of your own using a conjunction.

_____

Underline the conjunctions in these sentences.

1. I put the dog on the lead and we went out for a walk.

2. It felt cold although it was sunny.

3. We played in the park until it was dark.

4. Mum was cross when I got home late.

5. I missed my programme because it came on earlier than usual.

Write another sentence of your own using a conjunction.

_____

Sometimes we use **adverbs** to connect sentences and paragraphs so that our writing 'flows' better.

For example:
We were watching TV. Suddenly, all the lights went out.

Underline the adverbs that connect these sentences.

1. I missed the last five minutes of the film. Consequently, I don't know how it ended!

2. I can come to your house. However, I can't stay for long.

3. Firstly, you mix the butter and the sugar. Next, you add the egg.

4. Dad did the shopping. Meanwhile, Mum was at work.

5. Do your homework now. Later, you can go swimming.

Some connecting adverbs:

later

suddenly

finally

firstly

next

however

meanwhile

consequently

Write two sentences of your own and connect them using an adverb.

_____

_____

_____

_____

GET IT?

However is a connecting adverb.

Prefix

A **prefix** is a group of letters at the beginning of a word.

For example:
preschool
prehistoric

The prefix 'pre' means 'before' (in Latin).

Add prefixes to these words.

1. 'aqua' (means 'water' in Latin)

__ __ __ __ rium

__ __ __ __ tic

__ __ __ __ marine

2. 'viv' (means 'live' in Latin)

__ __ __ isect

__ __ __ acious

__ __ __ id

3. 'geo' (means 'Earth' in Greek)

__ __ __ metry

__ __ __ logy

__ __ __ graphy

4. 'bio' (means 'life' in Greek)

__ __ __ graphy

__ __ __ nic

__ __ __ logical

5. 'oct' (means 'eight' in Greek)

__ __ __ opus

__ __ __ agon

__ __ __ ave

6. 'super' (means 'over' or 'above' in Latin)

__ __ __ __ __ market

__ __ __ __ __ sonic

__ __ __ __ __ store

Suffix

A **suffix** is a group of letters at the end of a word.

Using a suffix can change the tense (from past to present tense and vice versa) or the meaning of a word.

Suffixes:

| -en / -ed | -ish | -ation | -less | -ment |
| -er / -or | -ing | -ful | -ly | -ness |

Add suffixes to these words.

1. instruct + or = _____
2. act + or = _____
3. conduct + or = _____
4. hope + less = _____
5. sleep + less = _____
6. rest + less = _____

7. excite + ment = _____
8. move + ment = _____
9. agree + ment = _____
10. immediate + ly = _____
11. sudden + ly = _____
12. extreme + ly = _____

When the root word ends in a vowel and you want to add a suffix that starts with a vowel, you drop one of the vowels.

Try these:
1. spice + ed = _____
2. care + ing = _____
3. late + er = _____

GET IT?

The vowels are: **a, e, i, o, u.** The other letters in the alphabet are called consonants.

Double the consonant when there is a single vowel before a single consonant, eg sit + ing = sitting.

Try these:
4. big + est = _____
5. swim + ing = _____
6. stop + ed = _____

Learn these:
beauty + ful = beautiful
happy + ness = happiness

Plural suffixes

Sometimes you just add an **s** to make a word plural (more than one). Other times you add **es**. How do you know when to add **s** or **es**?

If a word ends in **ch**, **sh**, **s**, **ss** or **x** you usually add **es**.

Try these:

wish   _____

kiss   _____

box   _____

lunch   _____

bus   _____

If a word ends in a consonant before a **y**, we drop the **y** and add **ies**.

Try these:

city   _____

pony   _____

memory   _____

dictionary   _____

baby   _____

Some words don't follow the rules!

You just have to learn them:

mouse – mice

child – children

man – men

woman – women

deer – deer

potato – potatoes

volcano – volcanoes

video – videos

Rhymes and alliteration

The way a word begins and ends is important when writing poetry.

Words that begin with the same sounds are called **alliterations**.

Words that end with the same sounds are called **rhymes**.

Read the poem:

> **My dog Dan,**
> **Chomps our shoes,**
> **Chases the cat**
> **And eats the news!**

1. Which two words rhyme in the poem? _____

2. Which words begin with the same sounds? _____

3. Write a list of words that rhyme with '**shoes**'.

_____

4. Choose one of these words to write an alternative last line.

_____

5. Write a short poem about an animal or a person that includes alliteration and rhyme.

_____

_____

_____

_____

Different kinds of writing

Diaries, letters, recounts and autobiographies are written in the **first person** using the pronouns I, my, mine and we.

Underline the first-person pronouns in this diary extract:

Somehow I knew that today was going to be special, even though it started off like every other day – I was going to be late for school again!

Instructions and advertisements are written in the **second person** using the pronouns you and your.

Underline the second-person pronouns in this instruction text:

To make chocolate brownies you need: flour, cocoa powder, eggs, butter and milk. But first, you need to find an adult to help you!

Novels, stories, information books and newspaper reports are written in the **third person** using the pronouns he, she, it and they.

Underline the third-person pronouns in this story extract:

"I'm so happy!" she said. "I want to thank everyone who voted for me!" They cheered enthusiastically as she lifted the winner's trophy.

Write three pieces of text – one in the first, one in the second and one in the third person.

LOOK FOR EXAMPLES IN BOOKS TO HELP YOU.

First person

_____

_____

_____

_____

Second person

_____

_____

_____

_____

Third person

_____

_____

_____

_____

GET IT?

There are two main types of writing. **Fiction** is not true; it is made up by the storyteller. **Non-fiction** is true; it is writing based on facts and real events.

Writing stories (fiction)

> When you write a story the first thing you need to decide on is where (and when) the action takes place – this is called the **setting**.

Writers often set their stories in places that are familiar to them, for example school, home, neighbourhood, workplace or somewhere they went on holiday.

Possible settings:

new school	raging river	remote rainforest
busy airport	noisy campsite	space station

Choose one of these settings and write notes on the mind-map below about the things you can see, hear, touch, taste or smell.

> USE A SEPARATE PIECE OF PAPER IF YOU NEED MORE SPACE TO WRITE.

> DECIDE WHETHER THE SETTING IS IN THE *PAST*, *PRESENT* OR *FUTURE*.

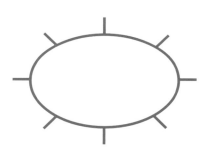

Characters are essential to tell the story.

Any characters you invent should have a clear purpose in the story and a distinct personality. They might be unusual in some way, eg in the way they dress or speak.

Match the following characters to the settings in the box above.
There are no right or wrong answers.

Polly Phonic – friendly, talkative	**Venus Strange** – clever, mysterious
Miss McEvil – controlling, ambitious	**Gazza Green** – loud, outdoorsy-type
Ace Bravado – dare-devil, adventure seeker	**Leif Biome** – wacky, curious nature

Now choose one of these characters and invent others to match your chosen setting.
Make up names and character descriptions. Use a separate piece of paper for this work.

All stories must have a **plot** or **theme** – this is what the story is about and what the characters do.

Here are some popular story ideas:

Possible plots:

good versus evil	a misunderstanding	a comedy
something is lost or stolen	journey of discovery	friendship theme

Choose a plot to match your setting and characters.

Write a story plan in five paragraphs:

Beginning – introduce your setting and characters

_____

_____

Build up – things start to happen and the plot develops

_____

_____

Crisis – a series of things go wrong, leading to a crisis

_____

_____

Solution – the characters manage to sort out the problem

_____

_____

Ending – the characters reflect on what has happened or changed

_____

_____

Now you are ready to write out your story in full!
Use a separate piece of paper for this.

Writing non-fiction

> Reports, recounts, instructions and discussions are examples of **non-fiction** writing.

Reports – writing about the facts known on a given topic. Use specialist vocabulary and define the terms used. Use a formal style in present tense. Illustrate with diagrams or pictures.

Recounts – writing about an event you have witnessed or an experience you have had. Use pronouns: I, we, he, she, they. Write in the past tense using powerful verbs. Use time connectives, for example then, when, later, next, eventually.

Instructions – writing about how to do something. Include lists of materials needed. Write a clear sequence of steps. Use verbs, for example cut, mix, stir, place. Use time connectives and pronouns such as you and your.

Discussions – writing about a topic to provide a balanced viewpoint or discussion. Write the points 'for' and 'against', using evidence to back up the argument. Use present tense and emotional language to engage with the reader. Reach a conclusion at the end.

Read the following report text:

Fast Cats

The cheetah is the fastest land animal. Cheetahs can reach speeds of up to 70 miles per hour (113 kph). They can accelerate faster than the average car: 0 to 60 miles per hour in only 3 seconds!

Their long legs and athletic bodies are built for fast acceleration. Wildebeest, their prey, are fast too but they are slower to accelerate. The cheetah, however, can't maintain this speed over long distances so sometimes the wildebeest manage to outrun them.

Larger cats such as leopards and tigers are slower because their bulkier bodies have to use more muscle and energy to propel them forwards. They can reach up to 35-40 miles per hour in short bursts.

Domestic cats can run up to 30 miles per hour. They have lost some of their speed because they no longer need to chase their dinner!

Now answer these questions in complete sentences:

1. What makes the cheetah so fast?

_____

_____

2. Is the cheetah faster than the fastest car?

_____

_____

3. How does the wildebeest manage to outrun the cheetah?

_____

_____

4. What is the opposite of a domestic cat?

_____

_____

5. What tense (past, present or future) is the text written in?

_____

_____

A discussion

Do dogs make good pets?

People have kept dogs as pets for hundreds of years. Dogs can be easily house-trained to live in our homes. They form loyal and protective bonds with their owners and for older people who live alone, a dog can provide companionship. Studies have shown that dog owners tend to be happier and healthier because the daily walks they give their dogs have health benefits for them also.

However, owning a dog comes with responsibilities. Dogs need feeding, exercising, love and affection, and someone to look after them when their owners go on holiday. One of the biggest complaints against dog ownership is dog-fouling. Despite fines of up to £1,000 there are still some irresponsible owners who do not clean up after their pets.

Dogs make good pets and they bring great rewards for many people but they bring responsibilities too which should not be forgotten. Dogs are not like toys given at Christmas that can be thrown away when we tire of them – a dog is for life.

GET IT?

The first paragraph outlines arguments 'for', the second paragraph outlines arguments 'against' and the final paragraph gives a conclusion.

Write a similar balanced argument: Do cats make good pets?* Use a separate piece of paper for this.

*Or any other animal you choose.

A recount

Read the following recount:

When I arrived home at 7 pm, I immediately knew something was wrong. The first thing I noticed was the light through the upstairs window when I knew I hadn't left it on. Then I saw that the front door was wide open! I stepped nervously into the hallway and everything looked okay. Next, I went into the living room and to my dismay I saw that some squatters had moved in! Then I called the police.

Now answer these questions in complete sentences:

1. What time connectives have been used in the text? List them below.

_____

2. What tense (past, present or future) is the text written in? Examine the verbs to find out.

_____

3. Is the text written in the first, second or third person? Explain your answer.

_____

Write a recount of a past event or experience that you can remember.
Use extra paper if needed.

_____

_____

_____

_____

_____

_____

Writing formal letters

WRITE YOUR ADDRESS HERE:

_____

_____

_____

THE RECIPIENT'S ADDRESS IS WRITTEN HERE:

The Manager
Pizza Palace
Garlic Street
Doughton
ET7 UP1

WRITE THE DATE HERE:

_____

Dear Sir/Madam,

WRITE A FORMAL LETTER TO COMPLAIN ABOUT THE LACK OF TOPPINGS ON A PIZZA YOU BOUGHT FROM A FAST FOOD RESTAURANT. MAKE IT CLEAR WHY YOU ARE WRITING THIS LETTER, E.G. DO YOU WANT A REFUND?

_____

_____

_____

_____

_____

Yours faithfully,

_____

WRITE YOUR SIGNATURE HERE:

GET IT?

If you know the name of the person you are addressing, you end with 'Yours sincerely'.

Answers

know your nouns
1. I hurt my knee.
2. The paint is still wet.
3. Don't touch the exhibits!
4. Red is my favourite colour.
5. Can I have a biscuit?
6. Let's go for a walk.

1. a pod of dolphins
2. a shoal of fish
3. a colony of ants
4. a crowd of people
5. a galaxy of stars
6. a fleet of ships
7. a clutch of eggs
8. a litter of puppies

perfect your pronouns
1. The reds beat the blues. They won by two points.
2. Jack loved the film when he saw it.
3. Bella is in my class. Do you know her?
4. Our neighbours are friendly when you get to know them.

1. The ice cream belongs to Amy. It's hers.
2. The snake belongs to us. It's ours.
3. The hat belongs to you. It's yours.
4. The car belongs to them. It's theirs.

adding adjectives
1. The <u>clever</u> detective caught the <u>notorious</u> thief.
2. <u>Spectacular</u> fireworks lit up the <u>dark</u> sky.
3. A <u>big, hairy</u> spider sat beside the <u>little</u> boy.

comparing adjectives
er	est
bigger	biggest
louder	loudest
funnier	funniest
healthier	healthiest

1. The triceratops was <u>heavier</u> than two elephants.
2. Energy-saving bulbs last <u>longer</u> than ordinary bulbs.
3. Wind energy is <u>greener</u> than oil.
4. Vegetables are <u>healthier</u> than cakes.
5. Of all the jellyfish, the box jellyfish is the <u>most deadly</u>.

verbs and adverbs
Here are some possible answers:
1. He looked fiercely at his opponent.
2. They spoke quietly on the phone.
3. She sang softly into the microphone.
4. The wind blew gently.
5. The volcano erupted violently.

playing with words
1. a ray of sunshine
2. a snake in the grass
3. a fly in the ointment
4. a night owl

1. Other people's lives always seem better than our own.
2. You risk losing everything if you put all your resources in one thing.
3. Two people might be able to solve a problem that one person cannot.
4. It is better to do something late than not at all.
5. Something can look flashy but not be valuable.

how to use apostrophes
1. the teacher's desk
2. Mum's purse
3. the artist's studio
4. the cat's whiskers

1. the girls' dog
2. the family's car
3. the players' changing room
4. the people's jobs
5. the babies' toys

1. We can't go yet.
2. She didn't like the taste.
3. The dog doesn't bite.
4. The car won't start.
5. It's not fair! / It isn't fair!

speech!

"I think Benji is sick," said Tom. "He won't eat his dinner."
"Perhaps he's not hungry," replied Tom's mum.
"But he's *always* hungry!" said Tom. "And it's his favourite: marinated chicken chunks in juicy jelly."

The position of the exclamation marks can vary depending on which words you want to emphasise. Here is one possibility:

"Mum!" shouted Tom.
"Now what?" said Tom's mum.
"I know why Benji won't eat his dinner," said Tom.
"It's a new recipe. They've added vegetables! You know he hates vegetables!"

clauses and conjunctions

Here are some examples:

1. Benji didn't eat his dinner so Bob ate it instead.
2. Benji and Bob were friends but they were rivals too.
3. Tom was worried when Benji didn't eat.
4. Mum wasn't paying attention because she was busy.

1. I put the dog on the lead <u>and</u> we went out for a walk.
2. It felt cold <u>although</u> it was sunny.
3. We played in the park <u>until</u> it was dark.
4. Mum was cross <u>when</u> I got home late.
5. I missed my programme <u>because</u> it came on earlier than usual.

1. I missed the last five minutes of the film. <u>Consequently</u>, I don't know how it ended!
2. I can come to your house. <u>However</u>, I can't stay for long.
3. Firstly, you mix the butter and the sugar. <u>Next</u>, you add the egg.
4. Dad did the shopping. <u>Meanwhile</u>, Mum was at work.
5. Do your homework now. <u>Later</u>, you can go swimming.

prefix

1. aquarium
   aquatic
   aquamarine

2. vivisect
   vivacious
   vivid

3. geometry
   geology
   geography

4. biography
   bionic
   biological

5. octopus
   octagon
   octave

6. supermarket
   supersonic
   superstore

suffix

1. instructor
2. actor
3. conductor

4. hopeless
5. sleepless
6. restless

7. excitement
8. movement
9. agreement

10. immediately
11. suddenly
12. extremely

1. spiced
2. caring
3. later
4. biggest
5. swimming
6. stopped

plural suffixes

wishes
kisses
boxes
lunches
buses

cities
ponies
memories
dictionaries
babies

rhymes and alliteration

1. shoes and news
2. chomps and chases, dog and Dan
3. shoes, chews, news, mews, blues, bruise, fuse, whose, cruise, hues, views. Did you think of any more?

different kinds of writing

Somehow <u>I</u> knew that today was going to be special, even though it started off like every other day – <u>I</u> was going to be late for school again!

To make chocolate brownies <u>you</u> need: flour, cocoa powder, eggs, butter and milk. But first, <u>you</u> need to find an adult to help <u>you</u>!

"I'm so happy!" <u>she</u> said. "I want to thank everyone who voted for me!" <u>They</u> cheered enthusiastically as <u>she</u> lifted the winner's trophy.

fast cats

1. The cheetah is fast because it has long legs and an athletic body.
2. The cheetah is faster than the average car.
3. The wildebeest can outrun the cheetah because it can maintain its speed over longer distances.
4. A wild cat is the opposite of a domestic cat.
5. The text is written in present tense.

a recount

<u>When</u> I arrived home at 7 pm, I <u>immediately</u> knew something was wrong. The <u>first</u> thing I noticed was the light through the upstairs window when I knew I hadn't left it on. <u>Then</u> I saw that the front door was wide open! I stepped nervously into the hallway and everything looked okay. <u>Next</u>, I went into the living room and to my dismay I saw that some squatters had moved in! <u>Then</u> I called the police.

1. The following time connectives are used: 'when', 'immediately', 'first', 'then' and 'next'.
2. The text is written in the past tense.
3. The text is written in the first person because the pronouns 'I' and 'my' are used.

Maths essentials

get to grips with maths

Number values

Write these numbers in words.

For example:
321,857 = three hundred and twenty-one thousand, eight hundred and fifty-seven

a. 53 _____

b. 653 _____

c. 1653 _____

d. 21,653 _____

e. 721,653 _____

Write these numbers in numerals.

a. Two thousand, three hundred and four _____

b. Nine thousand, one hundred and eighty _____

c. Eleven thousand, three hundred and seventy-six _____

d. Fifty thousand, six hundred and four _____

e. Two hundred and one thousand, eight hundred and ninety _____

Order these numbers from the smallest to the biggest.

a. 7436, 5345, 4201, 6032 _____

b. 5642, 5386, 5740, 5900 _____

c. 6945, 6201, 6001, 6389 _____

GET IT?

To order the digits, start from the left each time.

When you order decimal numbers, it can help if you line them up underneath each other.

For example:
0.60
0.06

0.60 is bigger than 0.06

GET IT?
0.06 is "nought point nought six".
0.60 is "nought point six nought".

Order these decimals from the smallest to the biggest.

a. 0.01, 0.90, 0.59, 0.73 _____

b. 0.10, 0.05, 0.21, 0.09 _____

Complete this number line with negative numbers.

-10   -8 -7   -5 -4   -1 0 1 2 3 4 5 6 7 8 9 10

Order these numbers as they would appear on the number line.

a. 9, 10, -1, -7, -3, -10 _____

b. 7, -7, 4, -2, -1, 9 _____

c. 5, 0, -1, 1, -8, -4 _____

Addition and subtraction

Add the units first, then add the tens, then the hundreds and finally the thousands.

Remember to carry digits over to the correct columns.

For example:

```
    Th  H  T  U
     1  4  5  5
+       2  3  5
_____
     1  6  9  0
              1
```

$5 + 5 = 10$ so carry the ten into the tens column.

Add these numbers.

a
```
    H  T  U
    5  7  3
+   3  3  5
_____
```

b
```
    H  T  U
    6  7  5
+   2  1  5
_____
```

c
```
  Th  H  T  U
   1  2  4  3
+  1  8  0  7
_____
```

d
```
  Th  H  T  U
   2  4  7  2
+  1  1  5  5
_____
```

e
```
  Th  H  T  U
   6  0  3  4
+  1  2  6  5
_____
```

f
```
  Th  H  T  U
   5  1  4  2
+  1  3  6  8
_____
```

Subtract the units first, then subtract the tens, hundreds and finally the thousands.

If you don't have enough units, exchange (or borrow) a ten for 10 units. If you don't have enough tens, exchange a hundred for 10 tens. If you don't have enough hundreds, exchange a thousand for 10 hundreds.

For example:

```
    Th   H   T   U
     0   15  12  1
     X   6   3   2
 -       7   4   5
 _____
         8   8   7
```

Subtract these numbers.

a
```
    H   T   U
    6   4   3
-   3   5   4
_____
```

b
```
    H   T   U
    6   7   2
-   2   2   4
_____
```

c
```
Th  H   T   U
 1  2   9   0
-   7   2   7
_____
```

d
```
Th  H   T   U
 2  2   8   9
-1  1   9   5
_____
```

e
```
Th  H   T   U
 3  7   7   7
-1  2   7   5
_____
```

f
```
Th  H   T   U
 4  0   2   4
-1  1   9   5
_____
```

GET IT?

Start from the right each time. You can exchange or borrow from the columns to the left.

1 ten = 10 units

1 hundred = 10 tens

1 thousand = 10 hundreds

Shapes

Learn the names of these 2-dimensional (2-D) shapes.

Can you draw lines of symmetry on each shape?

Parallelogram – opposite sides are equal and parallel

Trapezium – 2 sides are parallel

Square – 4 sides are equal, and 4 right angles

Rectangle – opposite sides are equal, 4 right angles

Regular pentagon – 5 equal sides, 5 equal angles

Regular hexagon – 6 equal sides, 6 equal angles

Rhombus – 4 equal sides, opposite sides are parallel

Kite – adjacent sides are equal, no sides are parallel

A **QUADRILATERAL** IS A SHAPE THAT HAS FOUR SIDES.

Answer: True (T) or False (F) below.

1. A square has 4 equal sides and 4 equal angles. ☐

2. A rectangle has equal opposite sides. ☐

3. A square is a quadrilateral. ☐

4. A trapezium has 1 line of symmetry. ☐

5. A rectangle has 4 lines of symmetry. ☐

Learn the names of these 3-dimensional (3-D) shapes.

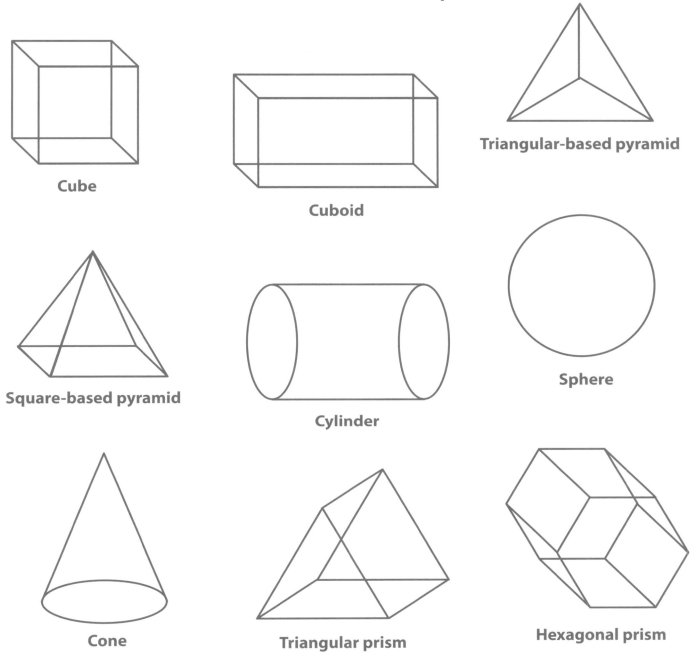

Cube

Cuboid

Triangular-based pyramid

Square-based pyramid

Cylinder

Sphere

Cone

Triangular prism

Hexagonal prism

Complete the table below:

Shape	Number of faces	Number of edges	Number of corners (vertices)
Cube			
Square-based pyramid			
Triangular prism			
Cuboid			

Multiples and factors

A **multiple** is the number you get when you multiply one number with another number, for example the multiples of 5 are 5, 10, 15, 20, 25, etc.

Count in 3s:

3 — 6 — ◯ — 12 — ◯ — ◯ — 21 — ◯ — 27 — ◯

Count in 4s:

◯ — 8 — ◯ — ◯ — 20 — 24 — ◯ — 32 — ◯ — 40

Count in 6s:

6 — 12 — ◯ — 24 — ◯ — 36 — ◯ — 48 — ◯ — 60

Count in 8s:

8 — 16 — ◯ — ◯ — 40 — 48 — ◯ — ◯ — 72 — 80

Circle the numbers that are multiples of 3. Which two numbers are also multiples of 6?

32   36   40   9   30   27   21

Circle the numbers that are multiples of 4. Which three numbers are also multiples of 8?

24   40   80   28   46   15   36

A **factor** is a number that will divide evenly (without a remainder) into another number, for example 3 is a factor of 6, 9 and 12, etc.

Find all the factors of 36:

1 x 36

2 x 18

3 x ___

4 x ___

6 x ___

Find all the factors of 24:

1 x 24

2 x ___

3 x ___

4 x ___

A **prime number** is only divisible by 1 and itself, for example 3 is a prime number.

Which of these are prime numbers? Circle them.

11   15   5   13   7   10   9   12

Work out what the missing numbers are.

For example:

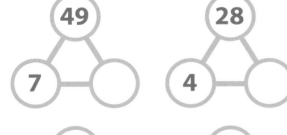

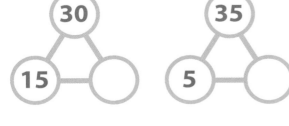

GET IT?

even x even = even

odd x odd = odd

odd x even = even

Division and multiplication

Complete the multiplication grid.

The first answer is done to get you started.

X	7	5	6	2
3	21			
6				
8				
4				

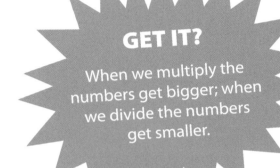

GET IT?

When we multiply the numbers get bigger; when we divide the numbers get smaller.

Multiplication and division are **opposites**.

For example:
8 x 5 = 40, so 40 ÷ 8 = 5 and 40 ÷ 5 = 8

Write two divisions to match each multiplication.

5 x 6 = 30

30 ÷ 6 = 5

30 ÷ ___ = ___

5 x 11 = 55

55 ÷ ___ = ___

55 ÷ ___ = ___

7 x 4 = 28

28 ÷ ___ = ___

28 ÷ ___ = ___

8 x 6 = 48

48 ÷ ___ = ___

48 ÷ ___ = ___

Division is like **repeated subtraction**.

For example:
55 ÷ 11 = 5   is the same as: 55 – 11 – 11 – 11 – 11 – 11

Work out these divisions.

30 ÷ 5 = ____

30 –

70 ÷ 10 = ____

70 –

56 ÷ 7 = ____

56 –

You can work out divisions using repeated subtraction on a number line.

For example:

12 ÷ 3 = __4__

12 11 10 9 8 7 6 5 4 3 2 1 0

Try it for yourself.

15 ÷ 3 = ____

15 14 13 12 11 10 9 8 7 6 5 4 3 2 1 0

20 ÷ 5 = ____

20 19 18 17 16 15 14 13 12 11 10 9 8 7 6 5 4 3 2 1 0

Perimeter and area

The **perimeter** is the distance around the edges of a shape.

Find the perimeter of these shapes.

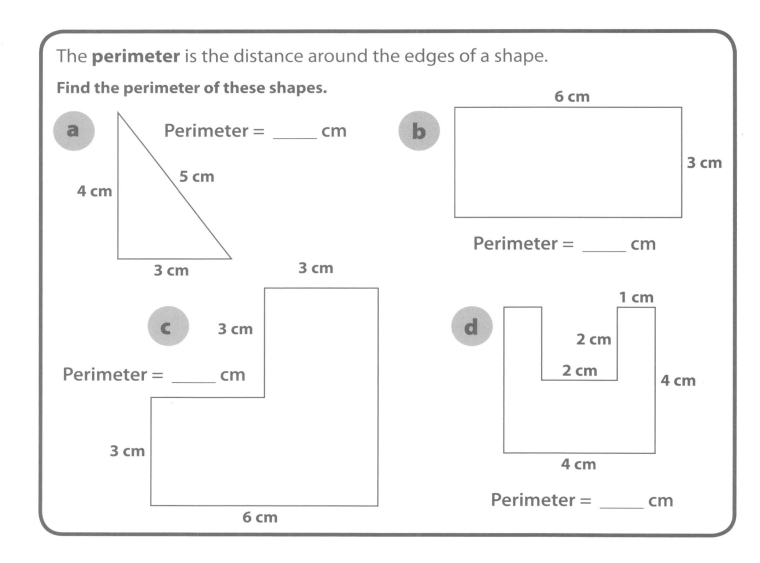

a Perimeter = _____ cm

4 cm   5 cm   3 cm

b 6 cm   3 cm

Perimeter = _____ cm

c 3 cm   3 cm

Perimeter = _____ cm

3 cm   6 cm

d 1 cm   2 cm   2 cm   4 cm   4 cm

Perimeter = _____ cm

Measure these shapes and find the perimeter.

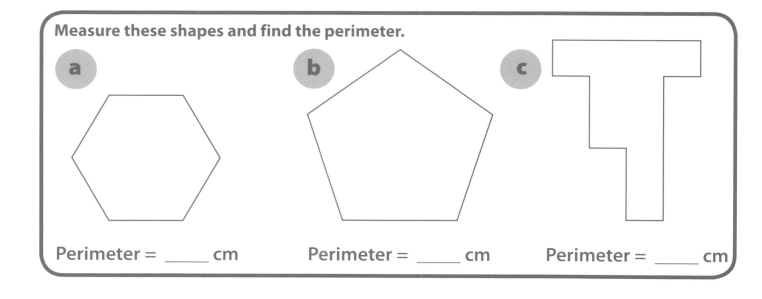

a Perimeter = _____ cm

b Perimeter = _____ cm

c Perimeter = _____ cm

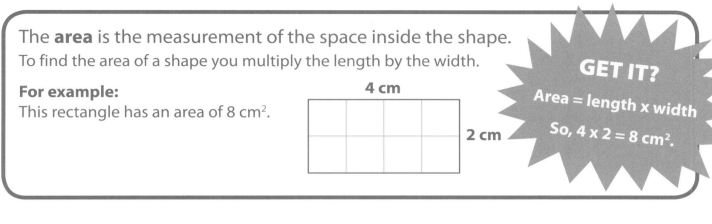

The **area** is the measurement of the space inside the shape.
To find the area of a shape you multiply the length by the width.

For example:
This rectangle has an area of 8 cm². 4 cm / 2 cm

GET IT?
Area = length x width
So, 4 x 2 = 8 cm².

Find the area of these shapes.

You might have to divide complex shapes into rectangles to work out the area.

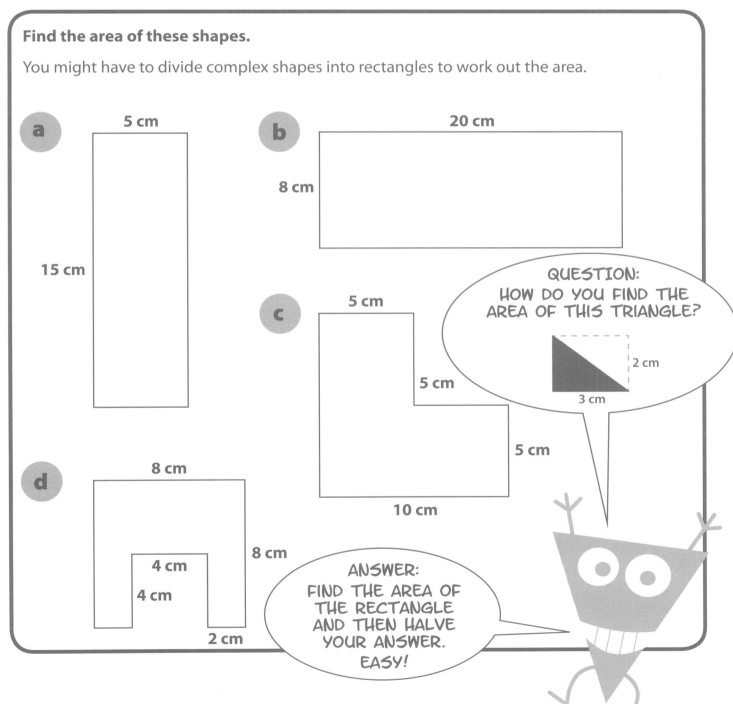

a   5 cm   15 cm

b   20 cm   8 cm

c   5 cm   5 cm   5 cm   10 cm

QUESTION:
HOW DO YOU FIND THE AREA OF THIS TRIANGLE?
2 cm
3 cm

d   8 cm   8 cm   4 cm   4 cm   2 cm

ANSWER:
FIND THE AREA OF THE RECTANGLE AND THEN HALVE YOUR ANSWER. EASY!

Fractions and percentages

$\frac{1}{4}$ means 1 part out of 4 equal parts.

$\frac{3}{4}$ means 3 parts out of 4 equal parts.

What fraction of these shapes is shaded?

 a

b

c

You can **simplify** fractions if you can divide the top number and the bottom number by the same factor.

For example:

$$\frac{2}{6} = \frac{1}{3}$$

Divide the numerator $2 \div 2 = 1$

Divide the denominator $6 \div 2 = 3$

THE TOP NUMBER IS CALLED THE **NUMERATOR**. THE BOTTOM NUMBER IS CALLED THE **DENOMINATOR**.

Simplify these fractions:

a. $\frac{4}{10} = $ ——   **b.** $\frac{3}{6} = $ ——   **c.** $\frac{8}{16} = $ ——   **d.** $\frac{4}{16} = $ ——

e. $\frac{5}{10} = $ ——   **f.** $\frac{2}{10} = $ ——   **g.** $\frac{3}{12} = $ ——   **h.** $\frac{4}{12} = $ ——

GET IT?

$\frac{6}{6}$ is one whole. $\frac{10}{10}$ is one whole. $\frac{12}{12}$ is one whole.

A **percentage** is a part of a hundred.

Learn these fraction and percentage equivalents.

10% or $\frac{1}{10}$									
20% or $\frac{1}{5}$									
25% or $\frac{1}{4}$									
50% or $\frac{1}{2}$									
100% or 1 whole									

Work out the answers.

a. $\frac{1}{2}$ of 50 = ____

b. 50% of 30 = ____

c. $\frac{1}{4}$ of 4 = ____

d. 25% of 8 = ____

e. $\frac{1}{5}$ of £2.50 = ____p

f. 20% of £5 = £____

g. $\frac{2}{5}$ of 25p = ____p

h. 40% of 30p = ____p

i. 10% of £4 = ____p

j. $\frac{1}{10}$ of £8 = ____p

GET IT?

1% is 1/100

10% is 10/100

20% is 20/100

Fractions

Colour $\frac{1}{4}$ of this circle red.

Colour $\frac{1}{2}$ of this circle blue.

What is the total fraction coloured?

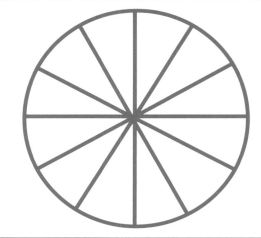

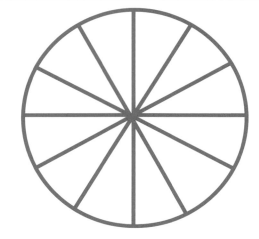

Which is bigger?

A slice that is $\frac{2}{3}$ or $\frac{3}{4}$ of this pizza?

Colour the pizza to work it out.

Which is bigger?

a. $\frac{5}{8}$ or $\frac{1}{4}$? ____

b. $\frac{3}{8}$ or $\frac{3}{4}$? ____

c. $\frac{4}{12}$ or $\frac{4}{6}$? ____

d. $\frac{5}{12}$ or $\frac{2}{3}$? ____

e. $\frac{4}{6}$ or $\frac{1}{3}$? ____

DRAW FRACTION PIZZAS TO HELP YOU!

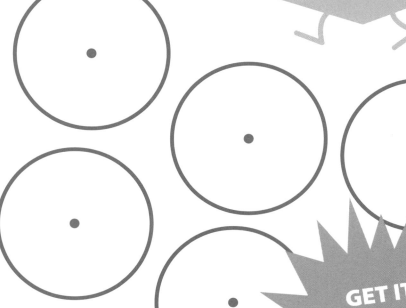

GET IT?

A **fraction** is an equal part of a whole.

Write these fractions in the correct place on the number line below.

0   **1**

$\frac{1}{2}$ $\frac{1}{5}$ $\frac{10}{10}$ $\frac{1}{10}$ $\frac{7}{10}$ $\frac{2}{5}$ $\frac{3}{10}$ $\frac{4}{5}$ $\frac{5}{10}$

Which two fractions have the same value?

Join the equivalent fractions with a line.

$\frac{2}{3}$ $\frac{2}{4}$ $\frac{3}{12}$ $\frac{3}{9}$

$\frac{4}{6}$ $\frac{1}{4}$ $\frac{1}{3}$ $\frac{1}{2}$

Order these fractions from the smallest to the biggest.

$\frac{1}{2}$ $\frac{1}{4}$ $\frac{3}{4}$ $\frac{4}{10}$

smallest
fraction

biggest
fraction

Angles and triangles

An **angle** is a rotation around a point.
We can measure an angle using a protractor.

There are four types of angles.

Right angle:
a quarter turn (90°)

Acute angle:
less than a quarter turn
(less than 90°)

Reflex: more than half
a turn (more than 180°
but less than 360°)

Obtuse: between a
quarter and a half turn
(more than 90° but less
than 180°)

* A complete rotation around a point is 360°.

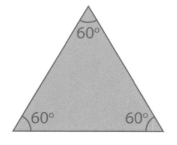

Equilateral: 3 equal sides
and 3 equal angles

Isosceles: 2 equal sides
and 2 equal angles

Scalene: no equal sides
and no equal angles.

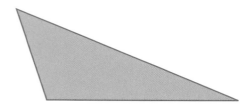

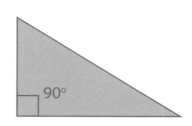

Right angled:
one right angle

If you add up the angles in a triangle you always get 180°.

Work out the missing angles in these triangles.

Label these angles: acute, right angle, obtuse or reflex.

a 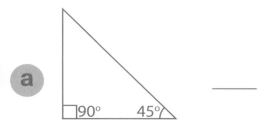 ____

a  _____

b 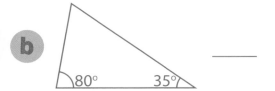 ____

b  _____

c  ____

c  _____

d 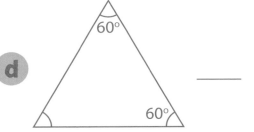 ____

d  _____

Find the angles.

a.  ____

b. ____

c.  ____

d. ____

Coordinates

Coordinates are the numbers we use to mark a point on a graph or map.

When reading coordinates, remember to *'go along the corridor and up (or down) the stairs'.*

Plot these positions on the graph.

a. (-2, 2)   **b.** (-4, 4)   **c.** (2, 2)   **d.** (4, 4)

e. (-2, -2)   **f.** (-4, -4)   **g.** (2, -2)   **h.** (4, -4)

GET IT?

Another way to remember how to read coordinates: x comes before y in the alphabet, so read the x axis first then the y axis.

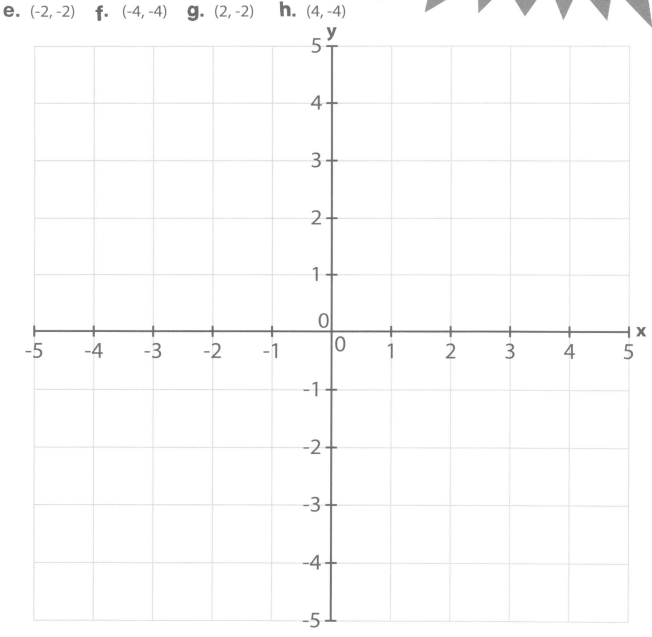

Write the coordinates of the big X: (_____ , _____)

Draw another X on the map and write its coordinates here: (_____ , _____)

Plot these coordinates to find a hidden shape.

(-4, -4) (-4, 2) (-2, 4) (-2, -2)

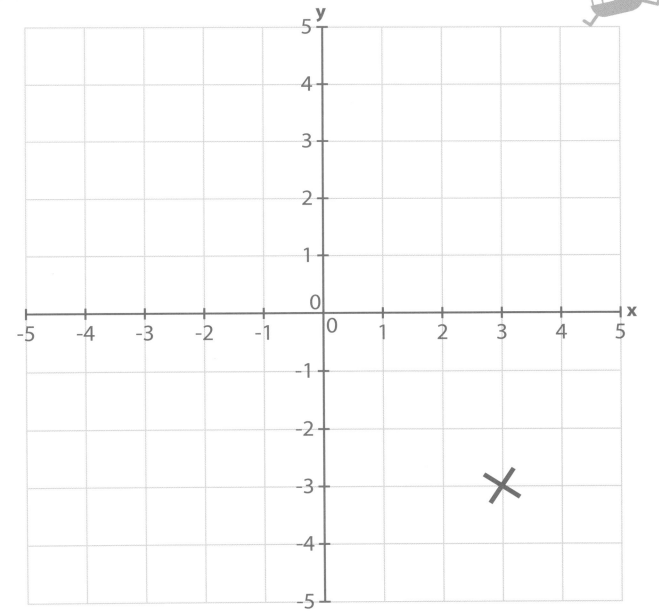

Long multiplication

Here are two methods of doing long multiplication.

For example:

```
H T U
  2 4 2
x   1 3
─────────
2 4 2 0  (x10)
  7 2 6  (x3)
─────────
3 1 4 6
```

Grid method:

X	200	40	2	Total
10	2000	400	20	= 2420
3	600	120	6	= 726

=3146

Find the answer to this multiplication using both methods.

```
H T U
  3 1 8
x   2 5
─────────
          (x20)

          (x5)
─────────
```

X	300	10	8	Total
20				=
5				=

=

BOTH METHODS SHOULD HAVE GIVEN YOU THE SAME ANSWER. WHICH DID YOU FIND THE EASIEST?

Find the answers to these multiplications using both methods.

Problem 1

```
  H  T  U
  3  2  6
x    1  2
_____
              (x10)

              (x2)
_____
```

X	300	20	6	Total
10				=
2				=

=

Problem 2

```
  H  T  U
  4  0  4
x    1  6
_____
              (x10)

              (x6)
_____
```

X	400	0	4	Total
10				=
6				=

=

Problem 3

```
  H  T  U
  2  1  3
x    2  4
_____
              (x20)

              (x4)
_____
```

X	200	10	3	Total
20				=
4				=

=

Long division

When you divide one number by another number, eg 28 divided by 7, it is like finding out how many 7s there are in 28. The answer is 4 because 4 x 7 = 28.

Look at this example:

$$7\overline{)2\ 8\ 7}$$

We know that 28 ÷ 7 = 4 so 280 ÷ 7 = 40

Then 7 ÷ 7 = 1

The answer = 41

We can write it down like this:

```
      4  1
7 | 2  8  7
  - 2  8  0
         7
```

Now look at this example:

```
      5  0  r 2
15 | 7  5  2        r = remainder
  - 7  5  0
         2
```

Try these divisions for practice.

GET IT?

75 ÷ 15 = 5 so 750 ÷ 15 = 50.

a  $20\overline{)4\ 8\ 0}$

b  $22\overline{)6\ 6\ 7}$

c  $14\overline{)5\ 7\ 4}$

d $50\overline{)2\ 6\ 0}$

Always try to estimate your answers first.

For example:

Share £2.04 between 4 children.

You know that £2 ÷ 4 = 50p so you can estimate that
£2.04 ÷ 4 will be a little bit more than 50p.

Now do the division to find out the answer ...

```
        5  1
  4 | 2  0  4
    - 2  0  0
            4
```
Answer: £2.04 ÷ 4 = 51p

Work out these division problems.

Estimate your answers first.

1. Share £5.25 by 5 children.

2. Divide 568 by 8.

3. 901 ÷ 4

4. If Alice can run 5 kilometres per day, how long would it take her to run 125 kilometres?

5. If Flopsy eats 156 carrots per year, how many carrots does he eat per week?

6. If Kipper sleeps 147 hours per week, how many hours does she sleep per day?

Do your working out here...

Now try dividing some longer numbers! Practise some divisions of your own.

For example:
```
          2  4  1
  12 | 2  8  9  2
     - 2  4           28 divided by 12 = 2 r 4
          4  9        49 divided by 12 = 4 r 1
        - 4  8
             1  2    12 divided by 12 = 1
```

Decimals

A **decimal** is part of a whole number. It is similar to a fraction.

The number before the decimal point is a whole number. The number after the decimal point is a part of a whole number.

Read the decimals on the number line below.

These are tenths of a whole number.

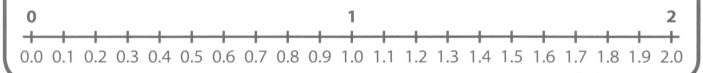

0 1 2

0.0 0.1 0.2 0.3 0.4 0.5 0.6 0.7 0.8 0.9 1.0 1.1 1.2 1.3 1.4 1.5 1.6 1.7 1.8 1.9 2.0

Circle the decimal that is bigger in each pair.

a. 0.2 or 2.0

b. 1.2 or 2.1

c. 2.4 or 2.9

d. 3.6 or 0.6

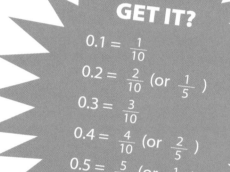

GET IT?

$0.1 = \frac{1}{10}$

$0.2 = \frac{2}{10}$ (or $\frac{1}{5}$)

$0.3 = \frac{3}{10}$

$0.4 = \frac{4}{10}$ (or $\frac{2}{5}$)

$0.5 = \frac{5}{10}$ (or $\frac{1}{2}$)

Add or subtract these decimals just as you would do with any numbers.

Put the decimal point in your answer.

a
```
   0 . 6
+ 0 . 7
_____
```

b
```
   1 . 5
+ 1 . 5
_____
```

c
```
   2 . 8
- 1 . 9
_____
```

d
```
   3 . 5 0
- 1 . 7 5
_____
```

We use decimals in money.

For example:

1p can be written as 0.01

5p can be written as 0.05

10p can be written as 0.10

50p can be written as 0.50

£1.50 can be written as 1.50

Multiply and divide these decimals.

For example:

```
£   2 . 5 0
x         6
_____
£ 1 2 . 0 0   (£2 x 6)
£     3 . 0 0   (50p x 6)
_____
£ 1 5 . 0 0
```

```
        3 . 2 0
      _____
    4 | £ 1 2 . 8 0
```

GET IT?

Try to estimate your answers first. Make sure you don't forget the decimal point – there is a big difference between £32.40 and £3240!

a. £2.25 x 4

b. £25.05 ÷ 5

c. £16.20 x 2

d. £28.21 ÷ 7

e. Share £14.40 by 6 children

f. 5 lots of 50p

Measures

Learn these equivalents:

1000 grams (g) = 1 kilogram (kg)

1000 millilitres (ml) = 1 litre (l)

1000 metres (m) = 1 kilometre (km)

1000 millimetres (mm) = 1 metre (m)

100 centimetres (cm) = 1 metre (m)

a. A cat can jump 2.5 m. How high is that in centimetres? _____ cm

b. A dog can run 5.4 km without stopping. How far is that in metres? _____ m

c. A quarter of a litre = _____ ml

d. 10 mm = _____ cm

e. Half a kilogram = _____ g

f. 1.50 kg = _____ g

g. 4.9 m = _____ cm

h. 3.2 litres = _____ millilitres

GET IT?

2.5 is the same as 2.50

5.4 is the same as 5.40

3.2 is the same as 3.20

a. Which is more: 1000 ml or 1 litre?   _____

b. What is 25 kg as grams?   _____ g

c. A fish tank holds 20 litres of water.
How many millilitres is that?   _____ ml

d. Benji weighs 10 kg. How much is that in grams?   _____ g

e. Tom's bowl holds 250 ml of milk. How many
bowls can be filled from 1 litre of milk?   _____ bowls

f. Write 1200 g as kilograms.   _____ kg

g. Convert 2.5 cm to millimetres.   _____ mm

h. Which is longer: 300 mm or 3 cm?   _____

i. Kevin has to run 8000 metres.
How many kilometres is that?   _____ km

j. Which is less: 250 ml or 2 litres?   _____

Moving the decimal

When we multiply a decimal number by 10 we move the decimal point **one** place to the **right**. When we multiply by 100 we move it **two** places. When we multiply by 1000 we move it **three** places.

For example:

4.9 x 10 = 49.00

4.9 x 100 = 490.00

4.9 x 1000 = 4900.00

We can leave out the zeros after the decimal point to simplify the number.

We do the opposite (we move the decimal point to the **left**) when we divide decimal numbers.

For example:

4.9 ÷ 10 = 0.49

4.9 ÷ 100 = 0.049

4.9 ÷ 1000 = 0.0049

Try these:

a. 1.35 x 10 = _____

b. 1.35 x 100 = _____

c. 1.35 x 1000 = _____

d. 1.35 ÷ 10 = _____

e. 1.35 ÷ 100 = _____

f. 1.35 ÷ 1000 = _____

GET IT?

If you run out of digits use zero as a place holder.

Answers

number values
a. fifty-three
b. six hundred and fifty-three
c. one thousand, six hundred and fifty-three
d. twenty-one thousand, six hundred and fifty-three
e. seven hundred and twenty-one thousand, six hundred and fifty-three

a. 2304
b. 9180
c. 11,376
d. 50,604
e. 201,890

a. 4201, 5345, 6032, 7436
b. 5386, 5642, 5740, 5900
c. 6001, 6201, 6389, 6945

decimals
a. 0.01, 0.59, 0.73, 0.90
b. 0.05, 0.09, 0.10, 0.21

negative numbers
-10 -9 -8 -7 -6 -5 -4 -3 -2 -1 0 1 2 3 4 5 6 7 8 9 10

a. -10, -7, -3, -1, 9, 10
b. -7, -2, -1, 4, 7, 9
c. -8, -4, -1, 0, 1, 5

addition and subtraction
add	subtract
a. 908	a. 289
b. 890	b. 448
c. 3050	c. 563
d. 3627	d. 1094
e. 7299	e. 2502
f. 6510	f. 2829

shapes
symmetry
The parallelogram has no lines of symmetry!

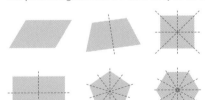

1. True
2. True
3. True
4. True
5. False

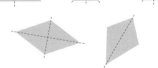

Shape	Number of faces	Number of edges	Number of corners (vertices)
Cube	6	12	8
Square-based pyramid	5	8	5
Triangular prism	5	9	6
Cuboid	6	12	8

multiples and factors
count in 3s: 3, 6, 9, 12, 15, 18, 21, 24, 27, 30
count in 4s: 4, 8, 12, 16, 20, 24, 28, 32, 36, 40
count in 6s: 6, 12, 18, 24, 30, 36, 42, 48, 54, 60
count in 8s: 8, 16, 24, 32, 40, 48, 56, 64, 72, 80

multiples of 3: 36, 9, 30, 27, 21
multiples of 6: 36, 30
multiples of 4: 24, 40, 80, 28, 36
multiples of 8: 24, 40, 80

factors of 36	factors of 24
1 x 36	1 x 24
2 x 18	2 x 12
3 x 12	3 x 8
4 x 9	4 x 6
6 x 6	

prime numbers: 11, 5, 13, 7

missing numbers
3 x 2 = 6
7 x 7 = 49
4 x 7 = 28
15 x 2 = 30
5 x 7 = 35

division and multiplication
X	7	5	6	2
3	21	15	18	6
6	42	30	36	12
8	56	40	48	16
4	28	20	24	8

5 x 6 = 30   5 x 11 = 55
30 ÷ 6 = 5   55 ÷ 11 = 5
30 ÷ 5 = 6   55 ÷ 5 = 11

7 x 4 = 28   8 x 6 = 48
28 ÷ 4 = 7   48 ÷ 6 = 8
28 ÷ 7 = 4   48 ÷ 8 = 6

repeated subtraction
30 ÷ 5 = [6]
30 − 5 − 5 − 5 − 5 − 5 − 5

70 ÷ 10 = [7]
70 − 10 − 10 − 10 − 10 − 10 − 10 − 10

56 ÷ 7 = [8]
56 − 7 − 7 − 7 − 7 − 7 − 7 − 7 − 7

subtraction on a number line
15 ÷ 3 = [5]   15 → 12 → 9 → 6 → 3 → 0

20 ÷ 5 = [4]   20 → 15 → 10 → 5 → 0

perimeter and area
a. 4 + 3 + 5 = 12 cm
b. 6 + 6 + 3 + 3 = 18 cm
c. 6 + 6 + 3 + 3 + 3 + 3 = 24 cm
d. 4 + 4 + 4 + 1 + 2 + 2 + 2 + 1 = 20 cm

a. 12 cm
b. 15 cm
c. 18 cm

area

a. 15 x 5 = 75 cm²

b. 20 x 8 = 160 cm²

c. 10 x 5 = 50 cm²
5 x 5 = 25 cm²
50 + 25 = 75 cm²

d. 8 x 4 = 32 cm²
2 x 4 = 8 cm²
2 x 4 = 8 cm²
32 + 8 + 8 = 48 cm²

area of the rectangle: 3 x 2 = 6 cm²
area of the triangle: 6 ÷ 2 = 3 cm²

fractions and percentages

a. 8 out of 16 parts = ⁸⁄₁₆ (or ½)

b. 4 out of 16 parts = ⁴⁄₁₆ (or ¼)

c. 3 out of 8 parts = ⅜

a. ⁴⁄₁₀ = ⅖	**b.** ³⁄₆ = ½	**c.** ⁸⁄₁₆ = ½
d. ⁴⁄₁₆ = ¼	**e.** ⁵⁄₁₀ = ½	**f.** ²⁄₁₀ = ⅕
g. ³⁄₁₂ = ¼	**h.** ⁴⁄₁₂ = ⅓	

a. ½ of 50 = 25	**b.** 50% of 30 = 15
c. ¼ of 4 = 1	**d.** 25% of 8 = 2
e. ⅕ of £2.50 = 50p	**f.** 20% of £5 = £1
g. ⅖ of 25p = 10p	**h.** 40% of 30p = 12p
i. 10% of £4 = 40p	**j.** ¹⁄₁₀ of £8 = 80p

fractions

⁹⁄₁₂ (or ¾) is coloured
¾ (or ⁹⁄₁₂) is bigger than ⅔ (or ⁸⁄₁₂)

a. ⅝ is bigger than ¼

b. ¾ is bigger than ⅜

c. ⁴⁄₆ is bigger than ⁴⁄₁₂

d. ⅔ (or ⁸⁄₁₂) is bigger than ⁵⁄₁₂

e. ⁴⁄₆ (or ⅔) is bigger than ⅓

number line fractions

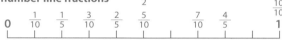

⁴⁄₆ = ⅔
³⁄₁₂ = ¼
³⁄₉ = ⅓
²⁄₄ = ½

smallest to biggest fraction: ¼, ⁴⁄₁₀, ½, ¾

angles and triangles

a. 90°, 45°, 45°	**a.** reflex	**a.** 45°, 315°
b. 80°, 35°, 65°	**b.** acute	**b.** 180°, 180°
c. 30°, 30°, 120°	**c.** obtuse	**c.** 90°, 270°
d. 60°, 60°, 60°	**d.** right angle	**d.** 270°, 90°

coordinates

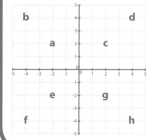

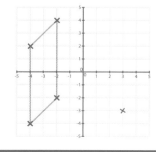

The coordinates for the big X are: [3, -3].
The coordinates [-4, -4] [-4, 2] [-2, 4] [-2, -2] form a parallelogram.

long multiplication

```
  H T U
  3 1 8
x     2 5
  ──────
  6 3 6 0  (x20)
  1 5 9 0  (x5)
  ──────
  7 9 5 0
```

X	300	10	8	Total
20	6000	200	160	= 6360
5	1500	50	40	=1590
				=7950

```
  H T U
  3 2 6
x     1 2
  ──────
  3 2 6 0  (x10)
    6 5 2  (x2)
  ──────
  3 9 1 2
```

X	300	20	6	Total
10	3000	200	60	= 3260
2	600	40	12	= 652
				=3912

```
  H T U
  4 0 4
x     1 6
  ──────
  4 0 4 0  (x10)
  2 4 2 4  (x6)
  ──────
  6 4 6 4
```

X	400	0	4	Total
10	4000	0	40	= 4040
6	2400	0	24	=2424
				=6464

```
  H T U
  2 1 3
x     2 4
  ──────
  4 2 6 0  (x20)
    8 5 2  (x4)
  ──────
  5 1 1 2
```

X	200	10	3	Total
20	4000	200	60	= 4260
4	800	40	12	= 852
				=5112

long division

a. 24

b. 30 r 7

c. 41

d. 5 r 10

1. £1.05 each

2. 71

3. 225 r 1

4. 25 days

5. 3 carrots per week

6. 21 hours per day

decimals

a. 2.0	**a.** 1.3	**a.** £2.25 x 4 = £9.00	**e.** £14.40 ÷ 6 = £2.40
b. 2.1	**b.** 3.0	**b.** £25.05 ÷ 5 = £5.01	**f.** 5 x 50p = £2.50
c. 2.9	**c.** 0.9	**c.** £16.20 x 2 = £32.40	
d. 3.6	**d.** 1.75	**d.** £28.21 ÷ 7 = £4.03	

measures

a. 2.5 m = 250 cm

b. 5.4 km = 5,400 m

c. 1000 ml ÷ 4 = 250 ml

d. 10 mm = 1 cm

e. 1000 g ÷ 2 = 500 g

f. 1.50 kg = 1500 g

g. 4.9 m = 490 cm

h. 3.2 litres = 3200 millilitres

a. 1000 ml and 1 litre are the same.

b. 25 kg = 25,000 g

c. 20 litres = 20,000 ml

d. 10 kg = 10,000 g

e. 1000 ml ÷ 250 ml = 4 (bowls)

f. 1200 g = 1.2 kg

g. 2.5 cm = 25 mm

h. 300 mm (or 30 cm) is longer than 3 cm

i. 8 km

j. 250 ml

moving the decimal

a. 1.35 x 10 = 13.5

b. 1.35 x 100 = 135

c. 1.35 x 1000 = 1350

d. 1.35 ÷ 10 = 0.135

e. 1.35 ÷ 100 = 0.0135

f. 1.35 ÷ 1000 = 0.00135

English
revision
revise and practise English

Revise your spellings

Read the word pairs. Tick the words that are spelled correctly.

always *or* allways

animul *or* animal

anuther *or* another

around *or* arownd

balloon *or* baloon

befor *or* before

being *or* bein

birthday *or* burthday

bruther *or* brother

can't *or* cant

chaing *or* change

children *or* childrun

comeing *or* coming

didn't *or* didnt

diffrent *or* different

does *or* dus

don't *or* dont

evry *or* every

father *or* fathir

first *or* furst

friend *or* frend

garden *or* gardan

gon *or* gone

great *or* grait

havf *or* half

head *or* hed

heard *or* hurd

I'm *or* Im

important *or* importent

jumped *or* jumpt

leave *or* leeve

light *or* lyte

money *or* munny

muther *or* mother

never *or* nevver

numbr *or* number

only *or* onely

uther *or* other

outside *or* owtside

paper *or* papeer

question *or* qestion

rownd *or* round

sisster *or* sister

sumthing *or* something

sometimes *or* somtimes

stopped *or* stoppt

suddenly *or* suddanly

swiming *or* swimming

thought *or* thowght

through *or* throuw

tried *or* tryed

usud *or* used

walked *or* walkt

white *or* whyte

whye *or* why

window *or* windoe

woke *or* woak

wurld *or* world

year *or* yeur

yung *or* young

Difficult spellings

Learn to spell more difficult words by breaking them down into syllables.

remember:

Syllables are groups of sounds that you can hear in words.

For example:

Steg- o- saur- us

There are four syllables in Stegosaurus.

Learn to spell these words by breaking them into syllables:

information _____

understand _____

Saturday _____

February _____

LOOK, SAY, COVER, WRITE, CHECK: LOOK AT THE WORD, SAY IT, COVER IT, WRITE IT, CHECK IT.

Learn to spell words in groups. Underline the parts of these words that are tricky to remember and learn to spell them.

famous	autograph
earring	solution
photograph	fabulous
pollution	stirring
jealous	paragraph
purring	position

Learn these 'ie' / 'ei' words:

field	receive
thief	ceiling
niece	seize ——— **'S' SOUNDS LIKE 'C'**
believe	eight
achieve	weight
retrieve	freight — **'EI' SOUNDS LIKE 'AY'**
friend	reign

remember:

'i' before 'e' except after 'c', or when it sounds like 'ay'.

THAT'S WEIRD!

There are a couple of exceptions to the rule, eg weird!
You will just have to learn to remember them.

remember:

Homonyms are words that sound the same but are spelled differently and have a different meaning.

Homonyms:

pear and pair	break and brake	there and their
right and write	where and wear	fair and fare

Make sure you know the different uses of these homonyms.

Now choose any four homonyms from the list and write a sentence for each.

1. _____

2. _____

3. _____

4. _____

Nouns, verbs and adjectives

Complete these sentences by adding nouns, verbs or adjectives.

1. I got a _____ for my birthday.

2. On Saturday, we are _____ to the _____.

3. I love _____.

4. Help! I'm _____.

5. The _____ dog _____ its tail.

remember:
Proper nouns are names of people, places (eg countries, cities, towns, rivers), days and months.

Re-write these sentences so that the proper nouns start with capital letters.

1. mrs jones is taking us swimming on friday.

_____

2. ben nevis is the highest mountain in great britain.

_____

3. The spanish flag is red and yellow.

_____

4. The river seine runs through paris, france.

_____

5. roald dahl is my sister annie's favourite author.

_____

Write some more nouns, proper nouns, verbs and adjectives here:

Nouns	Proper nouns	Verbs	Adjectives
_____	_____	_____	_____
_____	_____	_____	_____
_____	_____	_____	_____
_____	_____	_____	_____

Complete these collective nouns.

1. a shoal of _____

2. a flock of _____

3. a pack of _____

4. a crowd of _____

5. a pod of _____

WHAT DOES A LITTER OF KITTENS AND A GAGGLE OF GEESE HAVE IN COMMON? A *LITTER* AND A *GAGGLE* ARE COLLECTIVE NOUNS.

Think of a synonym (a similar adjective) for each of the following words.

The first one has been done for you.

1. nice – good, pleasant, polite, okay _____

2. angry – _____

3. curious – _____

Think of an antonym (an opposite adjective) for each of these words.

1. disappointed – _____

2. excited – _____

3. perfect – _____

Pronouns, adverbs and powerful verbs

Read these sentences and decide which one sounds the most interesting.

WEAK VERB

1. The dog **went** across the road.

BETTER VERB

2. The dog **ran** across the road.

VERB + ADVERB

3. The dog **ran quickly** across the road.

POWERFUL VERB

4. The dog **dashed** across the road.

The sentence with the powerful verb is the most interesting. It is better to use one powerful word rather than lots of weaker ones.

Read the following text. Replace the weak verbs and adverbs (underlined) with powerful verbs and adverbs.

Choose from the following:
livid, approaching, dashed, apologised, secured, shouted, escaped

The dog <u>ran</u> across the road. A car was <u>coming</u> and the dog's owner <u>called</u> out to it. Luckily, the dog and the driver <u>didn't have any</u> injury but the driver was <u>very angry</u>. The owner <u>said he was sorry</u> and <u>put</u> the dog on its lead.

Write appropriate adverbs in the spaces below.
The first one has been done for you. Try to use a different adverb each time.

remember:
Adverbs tell us more about verbs. They often end in –ly.

1. The snow fell <u>softly</u>.

2. The dog growled _____.

3. The ice melted _____.

4. The leaves _____ rustled.

5. I walked _____ down the stairs.

6. My heart was beating _____.

7. Her hand gripped me _____.

8. I held on to the reins _____.

remember:
These words are pronouns: I, he, she, it, we, us, you, they, them.

You can use pronouns to avoid repeating people's names in a text.

Write the missing pronouns in this story.
Then continue it in your own way:

Once upon a time, there was a nosy little girl called Goldie Looks. _____ was walking down the street one day (_____ was late for school, as usual) when _____ saw a house. _____ had a grimy, dusty door. Goldie pushed the door and _____ opened! Inside _____ saw three

_____

_____

_____

Revise your punctuation

Punctuation helps the reader understand what is written.
Writing is clearer when we write in sentences using full stops, capital letters, commas, semicolons, question marks, exclamation marks, speech marks, etc.

remember:

- A full stop (.) goes at the end of a sentence where we would pause.

- A comma (,) separates ideas within a sentence and items in a list.

- A semicolon (;) joins sentences or phrases that are closely connected.

- A colon (:) starts a list or a new idea.

- An apostrophe (') shows you who owns something.
  It also shows you where words have been shortened.

- A question mark (?) tells you that a question is being asked.

- An exclamation mark (!) shows surprise, humour or excitement.

- Speech marks (" ") tell you exactly what words are spoken.

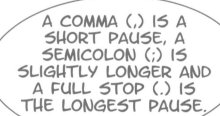

A COMMA (,) IS A SHORT PAUSE, A SEMICOLON (;) IS SLIGHTLY LONGER AND A FULL STOP (.) IS THE LONGEST PAUSE.

Add the missing punctuation to this story extract.

"Will you read me a spooky story?" Tim asked.

"Only if you promise to go to sleep afterwards," Tim's dad replied.

"Yes, I promise," said Tim.

His dad began to read. "It was almost midnight, the light of the full moon brushed the trees…"

Just when they got to the scariest part of the story, all the lights went out.

Then they heard a scary laugh. "Woah ah ah!" It was Mina, Tim's big sister, playing a trick on them.

"Dad," said Tim later, "I can't sleep. I'm too scared. Can you read me something happy instead?"

remember:
Start a new paragraph for each new speaker. Begin writing the paragraph after leaving a space at the beginning of the line.

Scary punctuation

Add the missing punctuation to these sentences.

1. The spell included the hair of a dog wings of a bat and a spiders web

2. Suddenly the door slammed shut

3. Its very dark in here she whispered

4. I think were trapped

5. Its a spell that I cant break she said

Use an apostrophe to shorten words in each of the sentences below.
The first one has been done for you.

6. I have written a ghost story.   I've written a ghost story.

7. It is so scary!   _____

8. You will have to read it.   _____

9. What is it called?   _____

10. The witch could not do any magic!   _____

Punctuation test

Add the missing punctuation to the following story text:

Will you call him killer, like your auntys old cat she asked

No he is much more handsome than old killer ever was

Yes he really is quite a cutie, and he has such

a sweet-tempered face and a softness around the

eyes – why dont you call him kitty

You will need:

3 pairs of speech marks ☐ ☐ ☐

2 question marks ☐ ☐

2 full stops ☐ ☐

2 commas ☐ ☐

3 capital letters ☐ ☐ ☐

2 apostrophes ☐ ☐

Tick the boxes ☐ *as you find the missing punctuation.*

1st, 2nd and 3rd person

The narrator is the person in the text who tells the story.

Change the pronouns (underlined) in this text from the first to the third person.

<u>I</u> was now beginning to grow handsome; <u>my</u> coat had grown fine and soft, and was bright black. <u>I</u> had one white foot and a pretty white star on <u>my</u> forehead.

Change the pronouns (underlined) in this text from the third person to the first person.

At this time <u>he</u> used to stand in the stable, and <u>his</u> coat was brushed every day till it shone like a rook's wing. It was early in May, when there came a man from Squire Gordon's who took <u>him</u> away to the Hall.

Extracts from 'Black Beauty' by Anna Sewell.

'BLACK BEAUTY' IS WRITTEN IN THE FIRST PERSON: THE HORSE, BLACK BEAUTY, NARRATES THE STORY. STORIES WRITTEN IN THE FIRST PERSON ENCOURAGE THE READER TO EMPATHISE WITH THE MAIN CHARACTER.

Read this job advertisement. It is written in the second person.

IF **YOU** LOVE HORSES THEN THIS IS THE JOB FOR **YOU**!

You can...

- help muck out the stables each day.
- groom and feed the horses.
- have **your** riding lessons for free!

*What are **you** waiting for? **You** can apply now!*

remember:
The pronouns 'you' and 'your' are speaking directly to the reader. Advertisers like to use these pronouns because they are friendly and persuasive.

Now it's your turn to write. Continue the following text:

A diary – in first person

Today _____

_____

An instruction – in second person

This is what you do: _____

_____

A description – in third person

She/he looked like _____

_____

_____

Limericks and poems

Use different colours to circle the words that rhyme.

There was an old man from Peru

Who dreamed he was eating his shoe.

He woke in a fright

In the middle of the night

And found it was perfectly true!

Anon

There was an old man with a beard,

Who said, "It is just as I feared –

Two owls and a hen,

Four larks and a wren

Have all built their nests in my beard!"

Edward Lear

Make up a limerick about a pet, someone you know or yourself.

Base it on the examples above.

_____

_____

_____

_____

_____

remember:

A limerick is a humorous verse of five lines, with the rhyming pattern: a, a, b, b, a.

Poetry can make us laugh, make us cry, or make us think.

Read this classic poem.

Hurt no living thing.

Ladybird, nor butterfly,

Nor moth with dusty wing,

Nor cricket chirping cheerily,

Nor grasshopper so light of leap,

Nor dancing gnat, nor beetle fat,

Nor harmless worms that creep.

Christina Rossetti

Write a poem in the style of 'Hurt no living thing'.
Choose your own animals and rhyming words.
Try to follow a similar rhyming pattern.

_____

_____

_____

_____

_____

_____

_____

I KNOW THE SHORTEST POEM IN THE ENGLISH LANGUAGE. IT'S CALLED 'FLEAS'.

Fleas

Adam 'ad 'em.

Similes and metaphors

Similes:

The moon shone **like** a torch.

He felt as strong **as** an ox.

Make up some of your own similes to complete these descriptions.

1. Some dinosaurs were as tall as _____

2. The longest dinosaurs were as long as _____

3. The smallest dinosaurs were like _____

4. Some dinosaurs had teeth like _____

Write your own metaphors to complete these descriptions.

1. She is a _____ in the swimming pool.

2. She is a _____ on the race track.

3. He is a _____ in the boxing ring.

4. He is a _____ on the skateboard.

Personification

Personification:

The sun smiled.

The grey sky wept.

The waves roared.

The spooky house groaned.

Make up some of your own personifications to complete these descriptions.

1. The road _____

2. The ships _____

3. The car _____

4. The computer _____

You can add an adjective before the noun if you want to.

POP!   BUZZ!   CRASH!   SQUELCH!   SQUEAK!

GLUG!   PLOP!

Complete each sentence below using an onomatopoeic word. The first one has been done for you.

1. The water sloshed on the floor.

2. The door _____

3. The gate _____

4. The plate _____

Powerful prefixes and suffixes

These prefixes and suffixes can change the meaning of the root word to its exact opposite.

For example:

truth**ful**   thought**ful**   cloud**y**
untrue   thought**less**   cloud**less**

Write one word from each pair (above) in these sentences.

1. It was a grey and _____ day.

2. She behaved in a cruel and _____ way.

3. The thief lied. His statement was _____ .

Choose from the remaining words to complete these sentences.

1. It was a bright and _____ day.

2. She behaved in a kind and _____ way.

3. The thief told the truth. His statement was _____ .

Add the prefix dis- to change these words.

agree

disagree _____

like

_____

appear

_____

honest

_____

obedient

_____

continued

_____

interested

_____

advantage

_____

loyal

_____

Write three sentences using any of the dis- words above. You can change the tense (with a different suffix) if you prefer.

1. _____

2. _____

3. _____

Change these words to mean more than one.

baby _____

memory _____

discovery _____

fox _____

cactus _____

fungus _____

wolf _____

knife _____

child _____

sheep _____

volcano _____

tomato _____

remember:

Suffixes can change words from singular to plural.

THERE ARE A COUPLE OF WORDS SET TO TEST YOU IN THIS LIST!

Proverbs and idioms

Write what you think these proverbs mean.

1. Birds of a feather flock together.

_____

2. The early bird catches the worm.

_____

3. Put your best foot forward.

_____

4. Don't cry over spilt milk.

_____

5. It never rains but it pours.

_____

Write what you think these idioms mean.

over the moon   _____

under the weather   _____

in the same boat   _____

touch and go   _____

high and mighty   _____

home and dry   _____

Write these sentences using standard (formal) English.

1. I won you in that race.

_____

2. It was him what done it.

_____

3. Let me lend your book.

_____

4. I'm the bestest.

_____

5. Me and my sister was lost.

_____

6. We was scared.

_____

7. Thems my shoes.

_____

8. Here's the lunch what I bought.

_____

remember:
You should use standard English in your writing at school – except perhaps in story writing when you want to make a character's direct speech sound more realistic.

Borrowed words

Some words we use are borrowed from other languages – this sometimes makes them more difficult to spell!

Words derived from French:

café

restaurant

hotel

beauty

garage

village

Words derived from Greek:

dinosaur

aqua

alpha

amphibian

geography

biology

Words derived from Latin:

decimal

adventure

century

vice versa

example (eg)

etcetera (etc)

remember:

Many scientific words come from Latin or Greek.

OTHER EXAMPLES ARE: ANNO DOMINI (AD), ANTE MERIDIEM (AM)! THAT'S WHY WE LIKE TO ABBREVIATE THEM!

Write some sentences using any of the borrowed words above – or any other borrowed words you know.

1. _____

2. _____

3. _____

4. _____

Terrible tenses

remember: Verbs change tense depending on when the action takes place.

For example:

To fly

Past: I flew

Present: I fly

Present (third person): He/she flies

Present continuous: I am flying

Future: I will fly

To swim

Past: I swam

Present: I swim

Present (third person): He/she swims

Present continuous: I am swimming

Future: I will swim

Write the verbs in the correct tense.

To think

Past: I _____

Present: I _____

Present (third person): He/she _____

Present continuous: I am _____

Future: I will _____

To write

Past: I _____

Present: I _____

Present (third person): He/she _____

Present continuous: I am _____

Future: I will _____

To eat

Past: I _____

Present: I _____

Present (third person): He/she _____

Present continuous: I am _____

Future: I will _____

To make

Past: I _____

Present: I _____

Present (third person): He/she _____

Present continuous: I am _____

Future: I will _____

Conjunctions

For example:

Kim loves sport. She hates swimming.

Kim loves sport **but** she hates swimming.

Conjunctions:

and	so	or	when
but	if	because	while

Use a conjunction to join two sentences into one sentence:

1. Dan and Kim are friends. They are always arguing.

_____

2. Kim usually wins. She shouts the loudest!

_____

3. Kim came home late last night. She's still asleep.

_____

4. Dan gets worried. Kim gets home late.

_____

For example: Kim snores when she is sleeping.

<u>Kim snores</u> is the main clause.

<u>when she is sleeping</u> is the subordinate clause.

Join each main clause to a subordinate clause to make one sentence with two clauses.

Main clause	Subordinate clause
1. Many mammals are intelligent	to hide from their enemies.
2. Baby mammals feed on their mother's milk	when they are born.
3. Some mammals have camouflage markings	and can learn to do new things.

Underline the main clause in each sentence below.

1. Mammals' bodies stay the same temperature whether it is hot or cold.

2. Some mammals grow a thicker coat in the winter months.

3. Some mammals like to live in groups when they are in the wild.

Connectives

Connecting adverbs:

after	now	later	finally	however
then	next	suddenly	firstly	consequently

Put these sentences in the correct order.

Look for the connecting words to help you. Number the sentences from 1 to 8.

☐ Next, their tails become shorter.

1 Frogs lay their eggs, called 'frog spawn', in water.

☐ After a few weeks tiny tadpoles hatch.

☐ First they grow their back legs.

☐ The tiny tadpoles breathe through gills, like fish.

☐ Then they grow their front legs at about ten weeks old.

☐ Finally they can jump out of the water and breathe air!

☐ Now they look like tiny frogs.

TOP TIP FOR BUDDING AUTHORS: A FAMOUS AUTHOR ONCE SAID, IT'S EASY; ALL YOU HAVE TO DO IS "PUT THE RIGHT WORDS IN THE RIGHT ORDER."

Now write out the sentences in the correct order below.

_____

_____

_____

_____

_____

_____

_____

_____

Active and passive verbs

For example:

The dog <u>chased</u> the cat. ——— ACTIVE

The cat <u>was chased by</u> the dog. ——— PASSIVE

The active sentence is about what the dog did.

The passive sentence is about what happened to the cat.

remember:
Some verbs can be **active** or **passive**.

Draw a line from the active to the passive text.

1. The dog picked up the scent.

2. Tom read the poem.

3. The mother carried the baby.

4. Molly made the cake.

The cake was made by Molly.

The baby was carried by the mother.

The scent was picked up by the dog.

The poem was read by Tom.

Write these sentences as passive text.

1. The snake ate the mouse.

_____

2. Harry won the prize.

_____

3. Some insects drink pollen.

_____

4. Plants and animals need oxygen.

_____

5. The girl wrote the scary story.

_____

Testing times

1. Where could you add a **semicolon** in this text?

She opened the cage door slowly in the darkness she could just make out the outline of an animal.

2. Underline the **pronouns** in this text. Is it written in first, second or third person?

Text this number for your chance to win this week's bonus prize – a holiday for two in a resort of your choice!

3. Underline the word that **connects** these two sentences.

The detective suspected this was a lie. However, he didn't cross-examine the suspect at this point.

4. Write the missing **colon** in this text.

You need to decide between these colours red, yellow, blue or green.

5. Write a list of your favourite things here, adding **commas** and/or **semicolons** to separate each item in the list. Write 'and' before the last item and end with a full stop.

_____

6. Replace the verb (underlined) for a more **powerful verb**.

Dinosaurs <u>walked</u> the Earth 65 million years ago.

7. Write a phrase containing a **possessive apostrophe** for each of the following.

the dog belonging to the family   _____

the sweets belonging to Jack   _____

the books belonging to the girls   _____

the goal belonging to the players   _____

8. Write these **contractions** in full.

wouldn't _____   he'll _____   it's _____

where's _____   that's _____   how's _____

answers

revise your spellings
These words are correct:

always	friend	question
animal	garden	round
another	gone	sister
around	great	something
balloon	half	sometimes
before	head	stopped
being	heard	suddenly
birthday	I'm	swimming
brother	important	thought
can't	jumped	through
change	leave	tried
children	light	used
coming	money	walked
didn't	mother	white
different	never	why
does	number	window
don't	only	woke
every	other	world
father	outside	year
first	paper	young

difficult spellings
in-form-a-tion
un-der-stand
Sat-ur-day
Feb-ru-a-ry

nouns, verbs and adjectives
1. Mrs Jones is taking us swimming on Friday.
2. Ben Nevis is the highest mountain in Great Britain.
3. The Spanish flag is red and yellow.
4. The River Seine runs through Paris, France.
5. Roald Dahl is my sister Annie's favourite author.

1. a shoal of fish
2. a flock of sheep
3. a pack of wolves
4. a crowd of people
5. a pod of dolphins

Here are some possible answers:
1. nice – good, pleasant, polite, okay
2. angry – cross, annoyed, livid
3. curious – interested, inquisitive, questioning

1. disappointed – pleased
2. excited – bored
3. perfect – imperfect

pronouns, adverbs and powerful verbs
The dog dashed across the road. A car was approaching and the dog's owner shouted out to it. Luckily, the dog and the driver escaped injury but the driver was livid. The owner apologised and secured the dog on its lead.

Once upon a time, there was a nosy little girl called Goldie Looks. She was walking down the street one day (she was late for school, as usual) when she saw a house. It had a grimy, dusty door. Goldie pushed the door and it opened! Inside she saw three …. (to be continued by you!)

revise your punctuation
"Will you read me a spooky story?" Tim asked.
"Only if you promise to go to sleep afterwards," Tim's dad replied.
"Yes, I promise," said Tim.
His dad began to read. "It was almost midnight; the light of the full moon brushed the trees…"

Just when they got to the scariest part of the story, all the lights went out!
Then they heard a scary laugh, "Woah-ah-ah!" It was Mina, Tim's big sister, playing a trick on them.
"Dad," said Tim later. "I can't sleep. I'm too scared. Can you read me something happy instead?"

scary punctuation
1. The spell included: the hair of a dog, wings of a bat and a spider's web.
2. Suddenly the door slammed shut!
3. "It's very dark in here," she whispered.
4. "I think we're trapped!"
5. "It's a spell that I can't break!" she said.
6. I've written a ghost story.
7. It's so scary!
8. You'll have to read it.
9. What's it called?
10. The witch couldn't do any magic!

punctuation test
"Will you call him Killer, like your aunty's old cat?" she asked.
"No, he is much more handsome than old Killer ever was."
"Yes, he really is quite a cutie, and he has such a sweet-tempered face and a softness around the eyes – why don't you call him Kitty?"

1st, 2nd and 3rd person
He was now beginning to grow handsome; his coat had grown fine and soft and was bright black. He had one white foot and a pretty white star on his forehead.

At this time I used to stand in the stable, and my coat was brushed every day till it shone like a rook's wing. It was early in May, when there came a man from Squire Gordon's who took me away to the Hall.

personification
Here are some possible answers:
1. The water sloshed on the floor.
2. The door slammed shut.
3. The gate creaked open.
4. The plate smashed.

powerful prefixes and suffixes
1. It was a grey and cloudy day.
2. She behaved in a cruel and thoughtless way.
3. The thief lied. His statement was untrue.

1. It was a bright and cloudless day.
2. She behaved in a kind and thoughtful way.
3. The thief told the truth. His statement was truthful.

disagree
dislike
disappear
dishonest
disobedient
discontinued
disinterested
disadvantage
disloyal

babies	wolves
memories	knives
discoveries	children
foxes	sheep
cacti	volcanoes
fungi	tomatoes

proverbs and *idioms*
1. People who share the same interests like to be together.
2. If you need to do something, do it straightaway.
3. Try your best.
4. Don't worry about things you can't change.
5. When bad things happen they come all at once.

over the moon – feeling very happy
under the weather – feeling unwell
in the same boat – in the same situation
touch and go – risky
high and mighty – behaving as if important
home and dry – safe

standard english
1. I beat you in that race.
2. He did it.
3. Let me borrow your book.
4. I'm the best.
5. My sister and I were lost.
6. We were scared.
7. They are my shoes.
8. Here's the lunch that I bought.

terrible tenses

I thought	I wrote
I think	I write
He/she thinks	He/she writes
I am thinking	I am writing
I will think	I will write
I ate	I made
I eat	I make
He/she eats	He/she makes
I am eating	I am making
I will eat	I will make

conjunctions
Here are some possible answers:
1. Dan and Kim are friends <u>but</u> they are always arguing.
2. Kim usually wins <u>because</u> she shouts the loudest!
3. Kim came home late last night <u>so</u> she's still asleep.
4. Dan gets worried <u>when</u> Kim gets home late.

conjunctions
1. Many mammals are intelligent and can learn to do new things.
2. Baby mammals feed on their mother's milk when they are born.
3. Some mammals have camouflage markings to hide from their enemies.

1. <u>Mammals' bodies stay the same temperature</u> whether it is hot or cold.
2. <u>Some mammals grow a thicker coat</u> in the winter months.
3. <u>Some mammals like to live in groups</u> when they are in the wild.

connectives
1 Frogs lay their eggs, called 'frog spawn', in water.
2 After a few weeks tiny tadpoles hatch.
3 The tiny tadpoles breathe through gills, like fish.
4 First they grow their back legs.
5 Then they grow their front legs at about ten weeks old.
6 Next, their tails become shorter.
7 Now they look like tiny frogs.
8 Finally they can jump out of the water and breathe air!

active and passive verbs

1. The dog picked up the scent.	The scent was picked up by the dog.
2. Tom read the poem.	The poem was read by Tom.
3. The mother carried the baby.	The baby was carried by the mother.
4. Molly made the cake.	The cake was made by Molly.

1. The mouse was eaten by the snake.
2. The prize was won by Harry.
3. Pollen is drunk by some insects.
4. Oxygen is needed by plants and animals.
5. The scary story was written by the girl.

testing times
1. She opened the cage door slowly; in the darkness she could just make out the outline of an animal.
2. It is written in the second person. Text this number for <u>your</u> chance to win this week's bonus prize – a holiday for two in a resort of <u>your</u> choice!
3. The detective suspected this was a lie. <u>However,</u> he didn't cross-examine the suspect at this point.
4. You need to decide between these colours: red, yellow, blue or green.
5. You can mark this one yourself!
6. Dinosaurs <u>roamed</u> the Earth 65 million years ago.
7. the family's dog, Jack's sweets, the girls' books, the players' goal
8. would not   he will   it is
   where is   that is   how is

Maths
revision

revise and practise maths

Number values

Each digit in a number has a **value**.

For example:
3450 = 3000 + 400 + 50 + 0

Remember:
9999 = 9000 + 900 + 90 + 9

Write the missing number values in the boxes.

a. 4098 = ☐ + ☐ + 90 + ☐   **b.** 5667   5000 ☐ ☐ ☐

c. 3824 = ☐ + 800 + ☐ + ☐   **d.** 1951 = ☐ + ☐ + ☐ + 1

Find out:

a. Which is more: 5 hundreds or 55 tens? _____

b. Which is less: 6 thousands or 61 hundreds? _____

c. What is the biggest number you can make with these digits: 2948? _____

d. What is the difference between: 98,430 and 97,430? _____

e. What do you need to add to 76,305 to make 76,605? _____

Write these numbers in figures.

a. Nine thousand, eight hundred and eight = _____

b. Eight thousand, six hundred and forty-two = _____

c. Three thousand, seven hundred and ninety-nine = _____

Work out the following:

a. 4590 ...+... 10 more is   __4600__

b. 8934 .... 10 less is   _____

c. 3193 .... 100 more is   _____

d. 6176 .... 100 less is   _____

e. 8321 .... 1000 more is   _____

f. 5869 .... 1000 less is   _____

Check out these numbers:

5000	five thousand
500	five hundred
50	fifty
5	five
0.5	nought point five
0.05	nought point nought five

Write these numbers in order from the smallest to the biggest.

Watch out for the decimals!

a. 5630, 521, 0.56, 5780, 540

_____ _____ _____ _____ _____

b. 6900, 0.06, 634, 691, 6999

_____ _____ _____ _____ _____

c. 0.70, 7809, 750, 0.07, 7001

_____ _____ _____ _____ _____

d. 8003, 0.83, 0.08, 855, 8300

_____ _____ _____ _____ _____

Addition and subtraction

Add these numbers in your head:

40 + 50 + 60 = _____   20 + 70 + 10 = _____

25 + 25 + 70 = _____   50 + 25 + 30 = _____

**When adding bigger numbers it
is easier to use a written method.**

For example:

	Th	H	T	U
		1	8	6	7
+			2	3	5
	2	1	0	2
		1	1	1

Add these numbers.

a

H	T	U
5	6	2
+ 2	3	8

b

H	T	U
3	8	7
+ 2	2	4

c

Th	H	T	U
3	4	6	3
+ 1	9	3	9

d

Th	H	T	U
5	8	4	6
+ 1	8	7	5

e Find the total of
460 + 13 + 7 + 3402

Th H T U

+ _____

f Find the total of
55 + 9 + 342 + 1348

Th H T U

+ _____

Try these subtractions.

For example:

```
        Th  H   T   U
        0  13  11   1
        X   X   X   3
    –       7   6   5
    _____
            6   5   8
```

remember:

Subtract the units first. Exchange (or borrow) from other columns if you need to, eg a ten for 10 units, a hundred for 10 tens and a thousand for 10 hundreds.

Subtract these numbers.

a
```
    H   T   U
    4   6   3
–   1   3   9
_____
```

b
```
    H   T   U
    2   3   5
–   1   4   9
_____
```

c
```
Th  H   T   U
2   3   6   4
– 1   8   5   7
_____
```

d
```
Th  H   T   U
4   5   2   1
– 1   8   7   5
_____
```

e
```
Th  H   T   U
3   7   6   5
– 1   9   7   5
_____
```

f
```
Th  H   T   U
5   3   4   2
– 1   6   9   5
_____
```

Decimals

A **decimal** is part of a whole number. It is similar to a fraction.

0.5 is the same as ½

1.5 is the same as 1½

We say:

0.5 = nought point five

1.5 = one point five

remember:

The number before the decimal point is a whole number. The number after the decimal point is a part of a whole number.

Write these decimals on the number line.

0.2   0.5   1.3   1.5   1.9   0.7   1.1   0.8

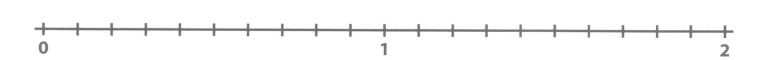

0   1   2

Write these numbers in order from the smallest to the biggest.

a. 7.3, 6.5, 9.2, 5.1

_____ _____ _____ _____

b. 96p, £1.06, £96, £1.96

_____ _____ _____ _____

MONEY IS WRITTEN IN DECIMALS – SO IT'S WORTH YOUR WHILE GETTING TO KNOW THEM!

c. 0.5 cm, 1.5 cm, 2.5 cm, 1.2 cm

_____ _____ _____ _____

d. 5.2 m, 5.5 m, 5.1 m, 5.9 m

_____ _____ _____ _____

Money and other measures, such as length, weight and volume, use decimals.

For example:

100 cm = 1 m   1000 g = 1 kg   1000 ml = 1 litre

150 cm = 1.5 m   1100 g = 1.1 kg   1900 ml = 1.9 litres

Find out:

a. How many pence in £2.50? _____ p

b. What is 673p in pounds and pence? £ _____

c. How many centimetres in 1.10 metres? _____ cm

d. What is 350 cm written in metres? _____ m

e. What comes next? 5.0, 5.2, 5.4, _____ , _____

f. What comes next? 7.1, 6.9, 6.7, _____ , _____

g. What is 1400 g in kilograms? _____ kg

h. How many millilitres in 1.4 litres? _____ ml

Decimals have fraction equivalents.

For example:

$0.50 = \frac{1}{2}$ $0.25 = \frac{1}{4}$ $0.20 = \frac{1}{5}$ $0.1 = \frac{1}{10}$ $0.01 = \frac{1}{100}$

PUT THESE FRACTIONS IN A CALCULATOR TO CHECK THE DECIMAL EQUIVALENTS.

remember:

0.50 is the same as 0.5

In money, 0.5 would be worth 50p.

0.05 would be 5p.

Draw a line to join each decimal to its fraction equivalent.

| 0.20 | 0.02 | 0.60 | 0.75 | 0.35 | 0.10 |

| $\frac{75}{100}$ | $\frac{35}{100}$ | $\frac{20}{100}$ | $\frac{2}{100}$ | $\frac{10}{100}$ | $\frac{60}{100}$ |

x and ÷ 10 and 100

> **Look for the pattern when you multiply by 10:**
>
> 5 x 10 = 50
>
> 50 x 10 = 500
>
> 500 x 10 = 5000
>
> **Look for the pattern when you divide by 10:**
>
> 50 ÷ 10 = 5
>
> 500 ÷ 10 = 50
>
> 5000 ÷ 10 = 500

Find out:

a. What is 6 x 10? _____

b. What is 15 x 10? _____

c. What is 330 x 10? _____

d. What is 70 ÷10? _____

e. What is 200 ÷ 10? _____

f. What is 4000 ÷ 10? _____

Solve these problems.

a. Each packet contains 10 biscuits. There are 15 packets in a carton. How many biscuits are in the carton?

_____ biscuits

b. Beans costs 80p per tin. Ben wants to buy 10 tins. How much money does he need?

£_____

c. A plain scarf costs £3. A patterned scarf costs ten times as much. How much is a patterned scarf?

£_____

d. If a dog drinks 1.5 litres of water a day, how much will 10 dogs drink?

_____ litres

remember:
1.5 litres is 1500 millilitres.

Look for the pattern when you multiply by 100:

5 x 100 = 500

50 x 100 = 5000

500 x 100 = 50,000

Look for the pattern when you divide by 100:

500 ÷ 100 = 5

5000 ÷ 100 = 50

50,000 ÷ 100 = 500

Find out:

a. What is 3 x 100? _____

b. What is 25 x 100? _____

c. What is 410 x 100? _____

d. What is 200 ÷100? _____

e. What is 1000 ÷ 100? _____

f. What is 2000 ÷ 100? _____

Calculate the following:

a. One-tenth of 120 is _____

b. One-hundredth of 700 is _____

c. Two-tenths of 60 is _____

d. Two-hundredths of 800 is _____

e. Five-tenths (or ½) of £1.50 is _____

f. Five-hundredths of £1 is _____

remember:

To find **one-tenth** (⅒) of something we **divide by 10**. To find **one-hundredth** (¹⁄₁₀₀) of something we **divide by 100**.

WHICH WOULD YOU PREFER? ONE-HUNDREDTH OF £100 OR FIVE-TENTHS OF £20?

Number sequences

Count in 3s to 30

Count in 6s to 60

Count in 9s to 90

WHAT DO YOU NOTICE ABOUT THE 3s, 6s AND 9s SEQUENCES?

Count in 2s to 20

Count in 4s to 40

Count in 8s to 80

WHAT DO YOU NOTICE ABOUT THE 2s, 4s AND 8s SEQUENCES?

Count in 5s to 50

Count in 10s to 100

WHAT DO YOU NOTICE ABOUT THE 5s AND 10s SEQUENCES?

Count in 25s to 250

Count in 50s to 500

WHAT DO YOU NOTICE ABOUT THE 25s AND 50s SEQUENCES?

Count on from 11 in 5s

_____

Count back from 53 in 5s

_____

Count on from 10 in 9s

_____

Count back from 88 in 9s

_____

Complete this multiplication square. Then colour in the multiples of 3. What do you notice?

1	2	3	4	5	6	7	8	9	10
2	4	6	8	10		14	16		
3	6		12		18	21		27	
4		12	16	20		28	32	36	40
5		15	20					45	50
6				30	36	42	48		
7		21						63	70
8	16			40	48	56			
9	18	27	36	45	54		72	81	90
10	20	30	40	50	60	70	80	90	

remember:
Subtracting 9 is easier if you subtract 10 first, then add 1.

Complete this multiplication square. Then colour in the multiples of 4. What do you notice?

1	2	3	4	5	6	7	8	9	10
2		6	8	10		14			
3	6		12			21	24	27	
4	8							36	40
5		15	20	25	30		40		
6			24					54	60
7	14			35	42	49	56		
8				48			64	72	80
9	18	27	36	45					90
10	20	30	40			70	80	90	

Fractions

A **fraction** is a part of a whole.

If we halve something, we divide it into two equal parts.

We write this as: $\frac{1}{2}$

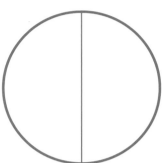

remember:

The number on top (called the **numerator**) represents the whole thing.

The number underneath (called the **denominator**) represents the number of parts.

Colour these fractions of the shapes.

1 Colour $\frac{1}{2}$

2 Colour $\frac{2}{3}$

3 Colour $\frac{2}{4}$

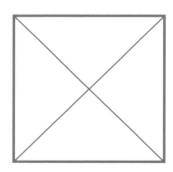

4 Colour $\frac{4}{5}$

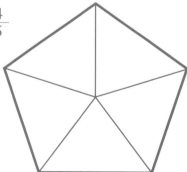

5 Colour $\frac{3}{6}$

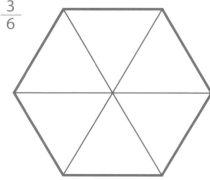

$\frac{2}{4}$ AND $\frac{3}{6}$ ARE THE SAME AS $\frac{1}{2}$!!

Fractions that have the same value are called **equivalent fractions**.

For example:

$\frac{1}{2}$ is the same as $\frac{4}{8}$, $\frac{5}{10}$, $\frac{6}{12}$ and $\frac{50}{100}$ etc.

Can you think of any other equivalent fractions? Write them in the space below.

Draw a ring around the fractions that are less than $\frac{1}{2}$.

$\frac{6}{14}$ $\qquad$ $\frac{3}{8}$ $\qquad$ $\frac{5}{10}$ $\qquad$ $\frac{9}{20}$ $\qquad$ $\frac{60}{100}$ $\qquad$ $\frac{7}{16}$ $\qquad$ $\frac{9}{12}$

Draw a ring around the fractions that are more than $\frac{1}{2}$.

$\frac{12}{20}$ $\qquad$ $\frac{7}{12}$ $\qquad$ $\frac{4}{8}$ $\qquad$ $\frac{9}{16}$ $\qquad$ $\frac{6}{18}$ $\qquad$ $\frac{6}{10}$ $\qquad$ $\frac{8}{24}$

Write these fractions in order from the smallest.

$\frac{1}{5}$ $\qquad$ $\frac{3}{4}$ $\qquad$ $\frac{1}{10}$ $\qquad$ $\frac{3}{6}$

___ $\qquad$ ___ $\qquad$ ___ $\qquad$ ___

remember:
You can simplify a fraction by dividing the top number and the bottom number by the same factor.

eg $\frac{12}{16}$ ($\div$ by 4) = $\frac{3}{4}$

What fraction of this shape is coloured?

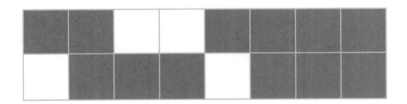

Shapes

Name these shapes.

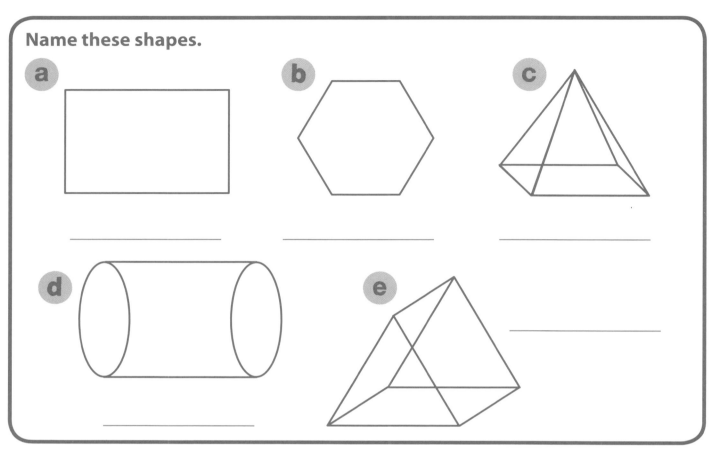

a

b

c

_____   _____   _____

d

e

_____

_____

Complete the following statement.

A cube has:

_____ faces.

_____ edges.

_____ corners (vertices).

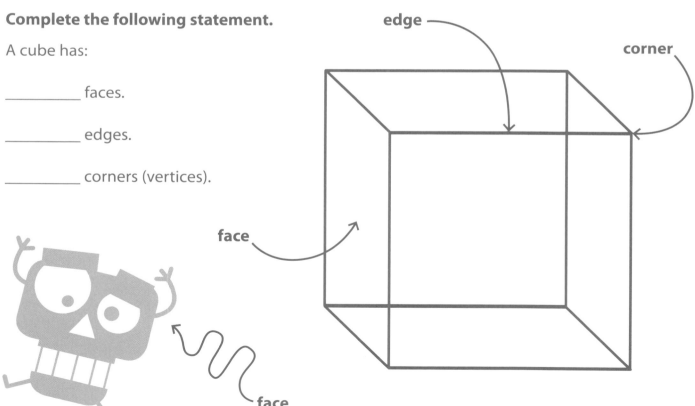

edge

corner

face

face

Write true (T) or false (F) next to each of these statements.

1. A triangle has 3 sides.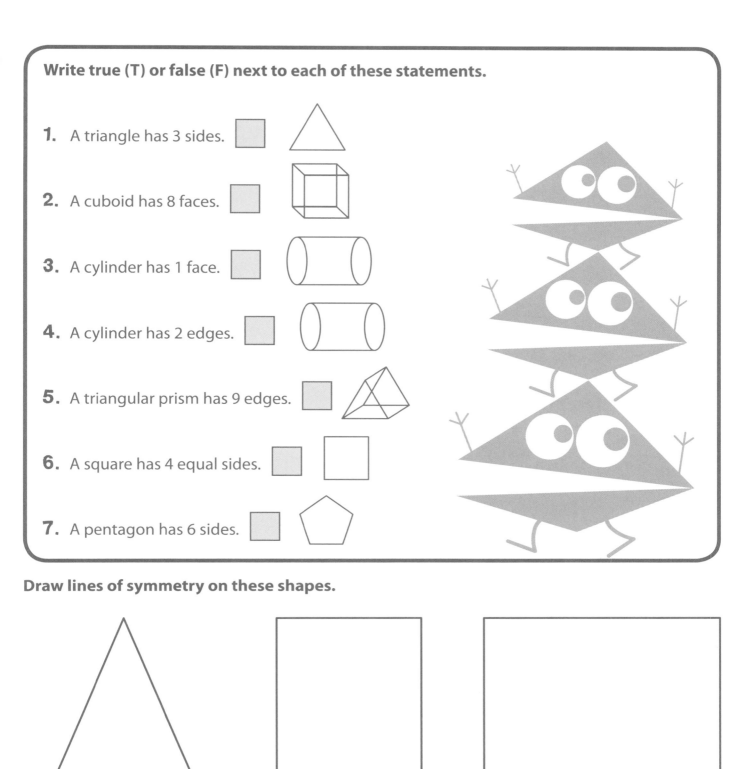

2. A cuboid has 8 faces.

3. A cylinder has 1 face.

4. A cylinder has 2 edges.

5. A triangular prism has 9 edges.

6. A square has 4 equal sides.

7. A pentagon has 6 sides.

Draw lines of symmetry on these shapes.

remember:
Some shapes have more than one line of symmetry.

Angles

An **angle** is a rotation around a point. We measure angles in **degrees** using a protractor.

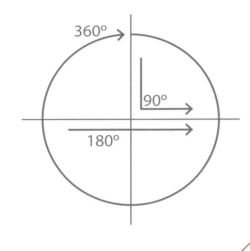

360 degrees = a circle

180 degrees = a straight line

90 degrees = a quarter-turn (a right angle)

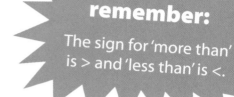

An angle **less** than 90 degrees is called **acute**.

An angle **more** than 90 degrees is called **obtuse**.

Label these angles 'acute' or 'obtuse'.

a _____

b _____

c _____

d _____

Calculate the unknown angle.

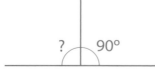

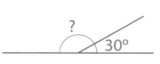

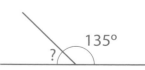

a _____

b _____

c _____

d _____

The angles in a triangle add up to 180 degrees.

60°

60°   60°

remember:
If you know two of the angles in a triangle you can calculate the third angle by subtracting from 180.

a ?

70°   70°

_____

b ?

60°   60°

_____

c ?

45°   90°

_____

d ?

100°   40°

_____

There are different types of triangle:

equilateral – 3 equal sides, 3 equal angles

isosceles – 2 equal sides, 2 equal angles

scalene – no equal sides, no equal angles

right-angled – one right angle

Identify these triangles using the definitions above.

a

_____

b

_____

c

d

_____

remember:
A right-angled triangle is labelled like this:

Multiplication

Multiply the numbers below using the following method.

For example: 56 x 7 = (50 x 7) + (6 x 7)

= 350 + 42

= **392**

Now it's your turn!

a 43 x 5 = (_____) + (_____)

= _____ + _____

= _____

b 28 x 3 = (_____) + (_____)

= _____ + _____

= _____

c 36 x 4 = (_____) + (_____)

= _____ + _____

= _____

d 69 x 10 = (_____) + (_____)

= _____ + _____

= _____

Multiply the numbers below using the grid method.

For example: **52 x 36**

X	50	2	Total
30	1500	60	= 1560
6	300	12	= 312

= **1872**

Give it a go!

a 27 x 34

X			Total
			=
			=

=

b 41 x 16

X			Total
			=
			=

=

Find the answers to these long multiplications using the following methods.

For example:

```
    1 4 2
x     2 6
---------
2 8 4 0   (x20)

    8 5 2   (x6)
---------
3 6 9 2
```

X	100	40	2	Total
20	2000	800	40	= 2840
6	600	240	12	= 852
				= 3692

a

```
    2 3 5
x     2 5
---------
          (x20)

          (x5)
---------
```

X				Total
				=
				=
				=

b

```
    4 1 6
x     2 7
---------
          (x20)

          (x7)
---------
```

X				Total
				=
				=
				=

c

```
    3 0 8
x     2 4
---------
          (x20)

          (x4)
---------
```

X				Total
				=
				=
				=

d

```
    2 3 2
x     3 2
---------
          (x30)

          (x2)
---------
```

X				Total
				=
				=
				=

Division

Division is the opposite of multiplication.

For example:

7 x 6 = 42   **So...**   42 ÷ 7 = 6 and 42 ÷ 6 = 7

Write two division facts for each multiplication below.

a. 8 x 10 = _____

_____

_____

b. 80 x 10 = _____

_____

_____

c. 50 x 5 = _____

_____

_____

d. 500 x 5 = _____

_____

_____

Dividing long numbers in your head is difficult so you need to learn a written method.

For example:

```
          3   4 r 1
    6 | 2  0   5
      - 1  8      (6 x 3)
         2  5
      -  2  4   (6 x 4)
            1
```

'R' MEANS REMAINDER!

remember:
Division is also like repeated subtraction.
E.g. 42 ÷ 6 = 42 – 6 – 6 – 6 – 6 – 6 – 6 – 6

 a

```
5 | 4  5  7
```

 b

```
3 | 6  0  4
```

c

```
2 | 1  5  6
```

 d

```
8 | 3  4  7
```

e

```
4 | 5  2  0
```

Always try to estimate your answers first when you are dividing.

For example: **300 ÷ 9**

You know that 300 ÷ 10 = 30 so you can estimate that 300 ÷ 9 will be a bit more than 30.

Now do the division to find out the answer …

```
          3  3 r3
    9 | 3  0  0
      - 2  7      (3 x 9)
         3  0
      -  2  7   (3 x 9)
            3
```

Work out these division problems.

Estimate your answers first.

1. Share £11.50 equally between Sam and Pam.

2. 720 divided by 3.

3. How many 150 cm ribbons can you make from 600 cm?

4. 696 ÷ 6

5. Share 2060 by 20.

6. How many groups of 8 are there in 448?

Do your working out here…

Rounding numbers

When making rough estimates in your head, rounding numbers (up or down) is useful.

For example, numbers from 101 to 104 can be rounded down to 100 and from 105 to 109 rounded up to 110.

Round these numbers to the nearest ten.

a. 21 _____

b. 687 _____

c. 453 _____

d. 999 _____

Area and perimeter

Area is a measurement of the space inside a shape.

If each square represents 1 square cm, what area is shaded?

_____ cm²

Perimeter is the distance around the edges of a shape.

What is the perimeter of the shape above? _____ cm

Draw your own shape in this space and find out its perimeter and area.

Find the area and perimeter of these shapes.

For example:

6 cm

2 cm

area = 2 x 6 = 12 cm^2

perimeter = 2 + 2 + 6 + 6 = 16 cm

a

14 cm

10 cm

area = _____ cm^2

perimeter = _____ cm

b

20 cm

4 cm

area = _____ cm^2

perimeter = _____ cm

c

15 cm

7 cm

area = _____ cm^2

perimeter = _____ cm

d

10 cm

30 cm

area = _____ cm^2

perimeter = _____ cm

What is the approximate area of this rectangle?

Round the decimals down or up to find out.

12.4 cm

19.7 cm

area = _____ cm^2

Coordinates

Coordinates are the numbers we use to pinpoint a place on a graph or map.

Look at the map below. You will find Skull Rock at (4, 5). Write the coordinates for the following:

a. Creepy cave (__ , __)

b. Stinky swamp (__ , __)

c. Skull and crossbones (__ , __)

d. Buried treasure (__ , __)

remember:
First you read along the x axis, then the y axis.

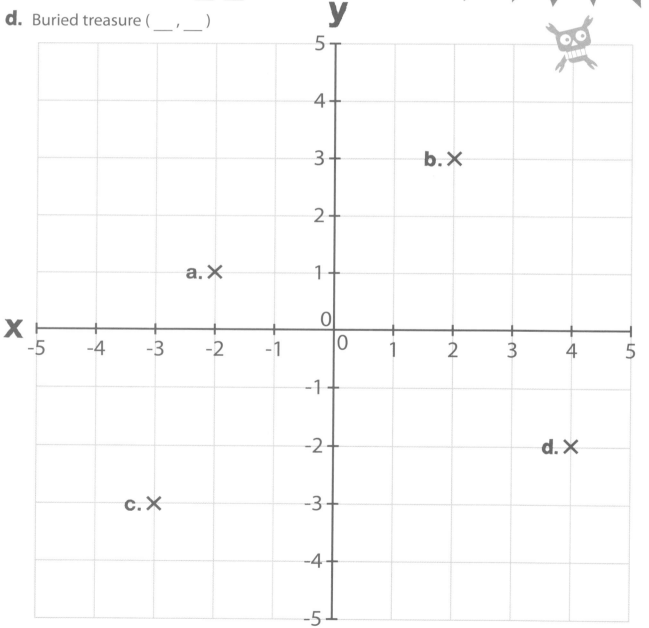

Draw your own treasure map with buried treasure.

Write the coordinates of the buried treasure here: (__ , __)

Write the coordinates for three other important places on your map.

Place name: _____ (__ , __)

Place name: _____ (__ , __)

Place name: _____ (__ , __)

Negative numbers

Complete this temperature scale.

Numbers on scale: -, -9, -, -, -6, -5, -4, -, -2, -1, 0, 1, 2, 3, 4, 5, 6, 7, 8, 9, 10

Use the number line to do these subtractions by counting back.

a. - 4 – 6 = _____

b. - 3 – 5 = _____

c. -1 – 4 = _____

d. 6 – 8 = _____

e. 2 – 5 = _____

f. 3 – 6 = _____

g. - 5 – 5 = _____

h. 9 – 17 = _____

i. 6 – 12 = _____

j. 2 – 10 = _____

remember:

$- 4 – 3 = - 7$

But $4 – 3 = 1$

BRRRR! IT'S FREEZING IN HERE.

YOU'RE SO NEGATIVE!

stick a reward sticker here!

Percentages

A **percentage** is a part of a hundred.

Revise these percentage and fraction equivalents:

$1\% = \dfrac{1}{100}$ (one-hundredth)

$10\% = \dfrac{10}{100}$ (one-tenth)

$25\% = \dfrac{25}{100}$ (one-quarter)

$50\% = \dfrac{50}{100}$ (half)

What percentage of each shape is shaded?

 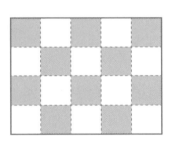

Now try these!

a. 50% of 100 = _____

b. 50% of 40 = _____

c. 25% of £1 = _____p

d. 10% of £1 = _____p

e. 10% of 50p = _____p

f. $\dfrac{1}{4}$ of 80 cm = _____cm

g. 25% of 1 kg = _____g

h. $\dfrac{1}{10}$ of 30 ml = _____ml

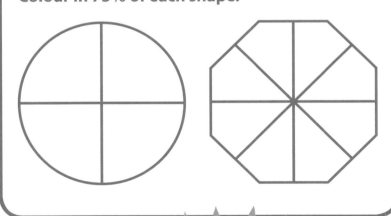

Colour in 75% of each shape.

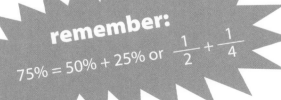

remember:

$75\% = 50\% + 25\%$ or $\dfrac{1}{2} + \dfrac{1}{4}$

Graphs

Look at the bar graph that shows the height of children in Class 6.

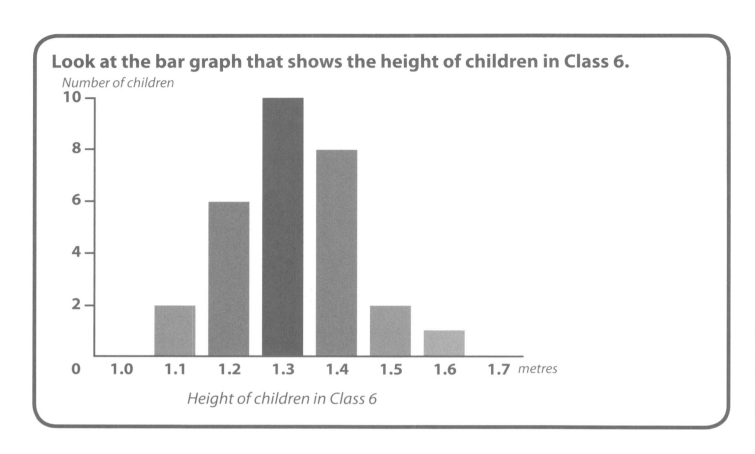

Number of children

Height of children in Class 6

Answer the following questions based on the graph.

a. What height are most children in Class 6? _____m

b. What is 1.2 m in centimetres? _____cm

c. What height are the shortest children in the class? _____cm

d. What is the difference in height between the shortest and the tallest child? _____cm

e. How many children are in Class 6? _____ children

WHO'S TALLER?

Look at the pie chart that shows the children's eye colours in Class 7.

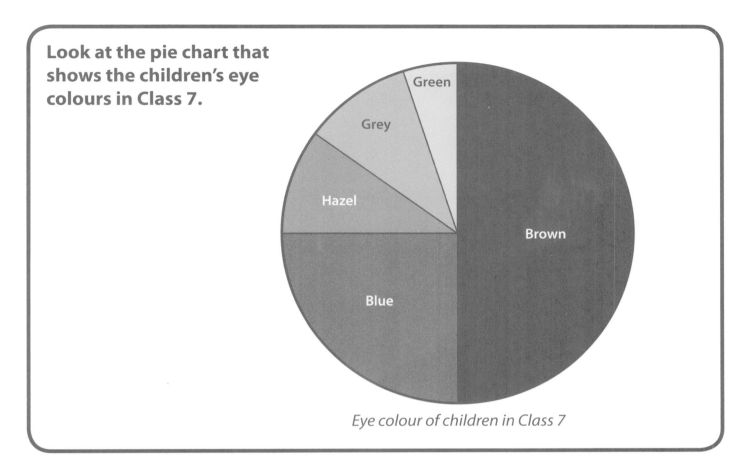

Eye colour of children in Class 7

There are 20 children in Class 7.

Answer the following questions based on the pie chart.

a. Which is the most common eye colour? _____

b. Which is the least common eye colour? _____

c. How many children have grey eyes? _____

d. What percentage of children have brown eyes? _____%

e. What percentage of children have blue eyes? _____%

LOOK INTO MY EYE!

Puzzles

1. Count all the squares you can find in this shape.

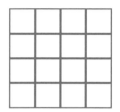

2. Complete this number sudoku so that each 3 x 2 block includes all the numbers from 1 to 6. The columns and rows must also include all these numbers.

3				1	4
	1	6			
	6	4	5		3
		2	4	6	1
6			3		
2	5				6

3. Complete these multiplication tables.

X	7	4	2	Total
3	21			= 39
	42			=
		32		=
5				=

X	6		9	Total
	36			=
7		70		=
			27	=
	30			=

4. Write the factors for each number on these spider diagrams.

a
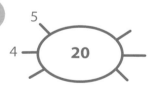
5
4
20

b
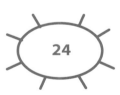
24

c

21

d
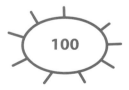
100

5. A short dog lead is 100 cm long. A long lead is 2 m. How much longer is the long lead in centimetres? _____ cm

Answers

number values

a. 4098 = 4000 + 0 + 90 + 8
b. 5667 = 5000 + 600 + 60 + 7
c. 3824 = 3000 + 800 + 20 + 4
d. 1951 = 1000 + 900 + 50 + 1

a. 55 tens is more
b. 6 thousands is less
c. 9842
d. 1000
e. 300

a. 9808
b. 8642
c. 3799

a. 4590 + 10 = 4600
b. 8934 – 10 = 8924
c. 3193 + 100 = 3293
d. 6176 – 100 = 6076
e. 8321 + 1000 = 9321
f. 5869 – 1000 = 4869

a. 0.56, 521, 540, 5630, 5780
b. 0.06, 634, 691, 6900, 6999
c. 0.07, 0.70, 750, 7001, 7809
d. 0.08, 0.83, 855, 8003, 8300

addition and subtraction

40 + 50 + 60 = 150
20 + 70 + 10 = 100
25 + 25 + 70 = 120
50 + 25 + 30 = 105

a. 800   **a.** 324
b. 611   **b.** 86
c. 5402   **c.** 507
d. 7721   **d.** 2646
e. 3882   **e.** 1790
f. 1754   **f.** 3647

decimals

a. 5.1, 6.5, 7.3, 9.2
b. 96p, £1.06, £1.96, £96
c. 0.5 cm, 1.2 cm, 1.5 cm, 2.5 cm
d. 5.1 m, 5.2 m, 5.5 m, 5.9 m

a. 250p
b. £6.73
c. 110 cm
d. 3.5 m
e. 5.0, 5.2, 5.4, 5.6, 5.8
f. 7.1, 6.9, 6.7, 6.5, 6.3
g. 1.4 kg
h. 1400 ml

0.20 = 20/100
0.02 = 2/100
0.60 = 60/100
0.75 = 75/100

0.35 = 35/100
0.10 = 10/100

x and ÷ by 10 and 100

a. 60
b. 150
c. 3300
d. 7
e. 20
f. 400

a. 150 biscuits
b. £8
c. £30
d. 15 litres

a. 300
b. 2500
c. 41,000
d. 2
e. 10
f. 20

a. One-tenth of 120 is 12
b. One-hundredth of 700 is 7
c. Two-tenths of 60 is 12
d. Two-hundredths of 800 is 16
e. Five-tenths (or ½) of £1.50 is 75p
f. Five-hundredths of £1 is 5p

number sequences

3s: 3, 6, 9, 12, 15, 18, 21, 24, 27, 30
6s: 6, 12, 18, 24, 30, 36, 42, 48, 54, 60
9s: 9, 18, 27, 36, 45, 54, 63, 72, 81, 90

The 3s sequence is half the 6s.
The 9s sequence is the 6s plus the 3s.

2s: 2, 4, 6, 8, 10, 12, 14, 16, 18, 20
4s: 4, 8, 12, 16, 20, 24, 28, 32, 36, 40
8s: 8, 16, 24, 32, 40, 48, 56, 64, 72, 80

The 4s sequence is double the 2s.
The 8s sequence is double the 4s.

5s: 5, 10, 15, 20, 25, 30, 35, 40, 45, 50
10s: 10, 20, 30, 40, 50, 60, 70, 80, 90, 100

The 10s sequence is double the 5s.

25s: 25, 50, 75, 100, 125, 150, 175, 200, 225, 250
50s: 50, 100, 150, 200, 250, 300, 350, 400, 450, 500

The 50s sequence is double the 25s.

11, 16, 21, 26, 31, 36, 41, 46, 51 and so on...
53, 48, 43, 38, 33, 28, 23, 18, 13, 8, 3
10, 19, 28, 37, 46, 55, 64, 73, 82, 91
   and so on...
88, 79, 70, 61, 52, 43, 34, 25, 16, 7

multiples of 3

multiples of 4

fractions

1.

2.

3.

4.

5.

These fractions are less than ½:
⁶⁄₁₄ ³⁄₈ ⁹⁄₂₀ ⁷⁄₁₆

These fractions are more than ½:
¹²⁄₂₀ ⁷⁄₁₂ ⁹⁄₁₆ ⁶⁄₁₀

These fractions are in order from the smallest: ¹⁄₁₀ ⅓ ³⁄₆ ¾

¹²⁄₁₆ (or ⁶⁄₈ or ¾) of the shape is coloured.

shapes
a. rectangle
b. (regular) hexagon
c. square-based pyramid
d. cylinder
e. (triangular) prism

A cube has:
6 faces
12 edges
8 corners (vertices)

1. True: a triangle has 3 sides.
2. False: because a cuboid has 6 faces.
3. False: because a cylinder has 3 faces.
4. True: a cylinder has 2 edges.
5. True: a triangular prism has 9 edges.
6. True: a square has 4 equal sides.
7. False: because a pentagon has 5 sides.

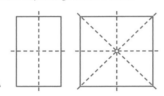

angles
a. obtuse
b. acute
c. acute
d. obtuse

a. 135°
b. 90°
c. 150°
d. 45°

a. 40°
b. 60°
c. 45°
d. 40°

a. isosceles
b. scalene
c. right-angled
d. equilateral

multiplication
a. 43 x 5 = (40 x 5) + (3 x 5)
   = 200 + 15
   = 215

b. 28 x 3 = (20 x 3) + (8 x 3)
   = 60 + 24
   = 84

c. 36 x 4 = (30 x 4) + (6 x 4)
   = 120 + 24
   = 144

d. 69 x 10 = (60 x10) + (9 x10)
   = 600 + 90
   = 690

a. 27 x 34

X	20	7	Total
30	600	210	= 810
4	80	28	= 108
			= 918

b. 41 x 16

X	40	1	Total
10	400	10	= 410
6	240	6	= 246
			= 656

a.
```
   2 3 5
x    2 5
4 7 0 0  (x20)
1 1 7 5  (x5)
5 8 7 5
```

X	200	30	5	Total
20	4000	600	100	=4700
5	1000	150	25	=1175
				=5875

b.
```
   4 1 6
x    2 7
8 3 2 0  (x20)
2 9 1 2  (x7)
1 1 2 3 2
```

X	400	10	6	Total
20	8000	200	120	=8320
7	2800	70	42	=2912
				=11,232

c.
```
   3 0 8
x    2 4
6 1 6 0  (x20)
1 2 3 2  (x4)
7 3 9 2
```

X	300	0	8	Total
20	6000	0	160	=6160
4	1200	0	32	=1232
				=7392

d.
```
   2 3 2
x    3 2
6 9 6 0  (x30)
  4 6 4  (x2)
7 4 2 4
```

X	200	30	2	Total
30	6000	900	60	=6960
2	400	60	4	= 464
				=7424

division
a. 8 x 10 = 80
   80 ÷ 10 = 8
   80 ÷ 8 = 10

b. 80 x 10 = 800
   800 ÷ 10 = 80
   800 ÷ 80 = 10

c. 50 x 5 = 250
   250 ÷ 5 = 50
   250 ÷ 50 = 5

d. 500 x 5 = 2500
   2500 ÷ 5 = 500
   2500 ÷ 500 = 5

a. 91 r 2
b. 201 r 1
c. 78
d. 43 r 3
e. 130

1. £5.75
2. 240
3. 4
4. 116
5. 103
6. 56 groups

Rounding numbers
a. 20
b. 690
c. 450
d. 1000

area and perimeter
The area of the shape is 12 cm².
The perimeter of the shape is 16 cm.

a. area = 140 cm²   perimeter = 48 cm
b. area = 80 cm²   perimeter = 48 cm
c. area = 105 cm²   perimeter = 44 cm
d. area = 300 cm²   perimeter = 80 cm

The area of the rectangle is approximately
12 x 20 cm = 240 cm².

coordinates
a. (-2, 1)   **b.** (2, 3)
c. (-3 , -3)   **d.** (4, -2)

negative numbers
a. - 4 – 6 = -10
b. - 3 – 5 = -8
c. -1 – 4 = -5
d. 6 – 8 = -2
e. 2 – 5 = -3
f. 3 – 6 = -3
g. -5 – 5 = -10
h. 9 – 17 = -8
i. 6 – 12 = -6
j. 2 – 10 = -8

percentages
a. ¹⁰⁄₂₀ or ½ or 50%
b. ⁴⁄₁₀ or ⅖ or 40%

a. 50% of 100 = 50
b. 50% of 40 = 20
c. 25% of £1 = 25p
d. 10% of £1 = 10p
e. 10% of 50p = 5p
f. ¼ of 80 cm = 20 cm
g. 25% of 1 kg = 250 g
h. ¹⁄₁₀ of 30 ml = 3 ml

graphs
a. 1.3 m   **a.** brown
b. 120 cm   **b.** green
c. 110 cm   **c.** 2 children
d. 50 cm   **d.** 50%
e. 29 children   **e.** 25%

puzzles
1. You should find at least 26 squares!

2.

3	2	5	6	1	4
4	1	6	2	3	5
1	6	4	5	2	3
5	3	2	4	6	1
6	4	1	3	5	2
2	5	3	1	4	6

3.

X	7	4	2	Total
3	21	12	6	= 39
6	42	24	12	= 78
8	56	32	16	= 104
5	35	20	10	= 65

X	6	10	9	Total
6	36	60	54	= 150
7	42	70	63	= 175
3	18	30	27	= 75
5	30	50	45	= 125

4. a. 20, 1, 10, 2, 5, 4
   b. 24, 1, 6, 4, 8, 3, 2, 12
   c. 21, 1, 7, 3
   d. 100, 1, 10, 20, 5, 25, 4, 50, 2

5. 100 cm